HSE
Health & Safety
Executive

A comprehensive guide to

Managing
ASBESTOS

in premises

HSE BOOKS

First published 2002
Reprinted 2004

ISBN 0 7176 2381 5

This guidance is issued by the Health and Safety Executive.
Following the guidance is not compulsory and you are free to
take other action. But if you do follow the guidance you will
normally be doing enough to comply with the law. Health and
safety inspectors seek to secure compliance with the law and
may refer to this guidance as illustrating good practice.

CONTENTS

Flow chart iv

Introduction 1
What does this guidance do? 1
Who this guidance for? 2
Background information for using this guidance 3
What does the law require? 8
What is asbestos? 10
The health effects of asbestos 10
Damaged asbestos 11
Where in premises can asbestos be found and what does it look like? 12

Developing an asbestos management strategy 17
Who should manage the ACMs on my premises? 17
Immediate action (steps 1-3) 17
Continuing actions (steps 4-7) 22

Case study 1: Local authority: London Borough of Islington 35

Case study 2: A National Health Service Trust: Tees and North East Yorkshire 39

Case study 3: A large chemical company: BP Chemicals 41

Case study 4: Facility management: Drivers Jonas facility management 43

Appendix 1: Planning surveys 47
What type of survey to carry out 48
Selecting a surveyor 49
Information gathering 50
Reporting format and medium 52

Appendix 2: Survey report, material assessment and algorithm 55
Survey report 55
Material assessment and algorithm 57

Appendix 3: Priority assessment and algorithm 59
Maintenance activity 59
Priority assessment algorithms 60

Appendix 4: Worked examples of priority assessments 63
Example 1: Primary school 63
Example 2: Chemical plant 68
Example 3: Hospital 74

Appendix 5: Management options and selection of management options 81
Management options 81
Measures needed in all cases where ACMs are present 81
Options for managing the condition of your ACMs 82
Selection of management options 85

Appendix 6: Managing asbestos contractors and analytical laboratories 91
Selecting licensed contractors 91
Asbestos removal work, what to expect 94
Asbestos removal methods 96
Enclosures 96
Viewing panels 96
Monitoring the contractor 97
Selecting analytical laboratories 97
Managing asbestos repair/removal contracts 98

References 99

Further information 101

Figure 1: Flow chart

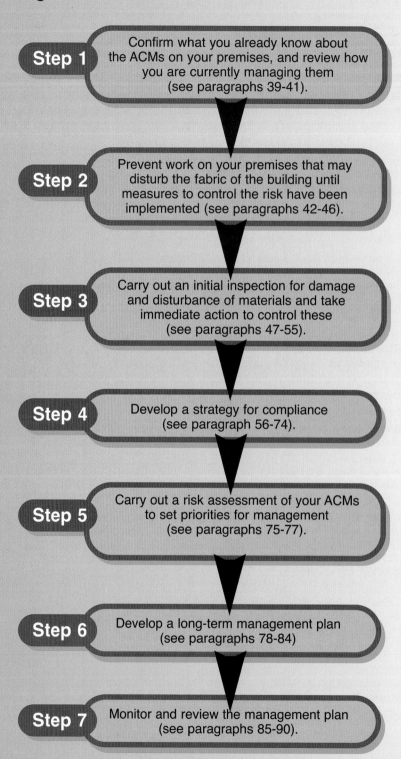

Step 1 — Confirm what you already know about the ACMs on your premises, and review how you are currently managing them (see paragraphs 39-41).

Step 2 — Prevent work on your premises that may disturb the fabric of the building until measures to control the risk have been implemented (see paragraphs 42-46).

Step 3 — Carry out an initial inspection for damage and disturbance of materials and take immediate action to control these (see paragraphs 47-55).

Step 4 — Develop a strategy for compliance (see paragraph 56-74).

Step 5 — Carry out a risk assessment of your ACMs to set priorities for management (see paragraphs 75-77).

Step 6 — Develop a long-term management plan (see paragraphs 78-84)

Step 7 — Monitor and review the management plan (see paragraphs 85-90).

FLOW CHART

The flow chart and these explanatory notes provide a general overview of the actions that you may need to take immediately and continuing actions that you may also need to take to effectively manage your asbestos-containing materials (ACMs). The extent to which you will need to carry out these actions will depend on your current management of ACMs and the size and complexity of your premises. Larger, more complex premises are likely to need to take all these steps to effectively manage their ACMs, whereas small and straightforward premises should be able to do less. Paragraphs 6 to 9 provide advice on what is likely to be required for small and straightforward premises, for example, a small retail premises.

Immediate actions

Steps 1 to 3 are the initial steps you should take to protect the health of your employees and others. They are designed to help you stop ACMs being damaged and disturbed *now* (Step 2), and *immediately* find any ACMs that are already damaged (Step 3).

- **Step 1: Confirm what you already know about the ACMs on your premises, and review how you are currently managing them (see paragraphs 39-41).**
  Reading these steps and the guidance in full will help you to do this. This will help you to decide how much more you need to do to manage your ACMs and will provide information to assist you in doing this.

- **Step 2: Prevent work on your premises that may disturb the fabric of the building until measures to control the risk have been implemented (see paragraphs 42-46).**
  The purpose of this step is to make sure that workers do not work on ACMs with out taking the proper precautions. This means any work, such as drilling, breaking, removing, sawing etc that could disturb the material. You should therefore not allow any work on the fabric of any building under your control, including piperuns, undercrofts etc, until you have put in place measures to control the risk. These will be short-term measures, until you have developed and implemented your management strategy.

Flow chart

- **Step 3: Carry out an initial inspection for damage and disturbance of materials and take immediate action to control these (see paragraphs 47-55).** This step is asking you to inspect your premises for damaged materials that may contain asbestos. Workers, during routine day-to-day activities, may be exposed to asbestos disturbed into the air they breathe if they or others disturb ACMs. This is a quick inspection to find out whether there are any problems that need dealing with now, but it is not intended to constitute a full assessment for the presence of asbestos on your premises. Typical examples to look out for include significantly damaged wall or door panels, or pipework insulation that has deteriorated or been damaged. If you find any damaged materials, you should consider whether they contain asbestos and take appropriate action to remove, repair or isolate them. If you find many, you may need to prioritise these using the algorithms referred to in Step 5.

Continuing actions

- **Step 4: Develop a strategy for compliance (see paragraph 56-74).** Steps 2 and 3 looked at minimising any immediate risks to health. You should now have stopped uncontrolled work on ACMs and found any damaged ACMs. You may still not know where all your ACMs are. In time, you will have to know where they are, or presume they are in places where you cannot conclude they are not. Managing asbestos means preventing your employees and others from breathing in asbestos fibres. Assessing your employees' and others' exposure to asbestos and therefore complying with your legal duties can be achieved in different ways.

  - You could survey your premises, identify all ACMs, take any necessary actions and put in place a system to manage your remaining ACMs.

  - Alternatively you could simply presume that all your building materials contain asbestos and when any maintenance or building work is needed, take a sample (see page 7) of the material for analysis, or work on it as if it was asbestos. You may still have carried out a damage and disturbance inspection as in Step 2.

  - You could use/obtain other strong evidence (such as plans and building specifications) that show the materials, or some buildings do not contain asbestos. You would need to be certain for these materials or buildings that the information is accurate and up to date.

  - You could do a combination of these. Survey and/or sample in some buildings or parts of buildings and leave others, depending on their occupancy.

- **Step 5: Carry out a risk assessment of your ACMs to set priorities for management (see paragraphs 75-77).** If you have carried out survey work, either determining whether materials contain asbestos or identifying those that may do so, you will need to set priorities for risk management. You may have found materials that need to be repaired or removed as a result of their condition or because of future planned work (eg refurbishment). You may not be able to tackle these all at once and therefore need to set priorities. Algorithms (see paragraphs 14-17) are provided to help you with this. You may also find these useful for setting priorities if you have found several ACMs requiring action during your 'damage and disturbance inspection' (Step 3).

- **Step 6: Develop a long-term management plan (see paragraphs 78-84).**
  The above steps should have taken you a long way towards preventing exposure to asbestos. But, you need to ensure that you continue to manage your ACMs, ensuring that you know the condition and location of all your ACMs in the long term and that this information is passed on to those liable to disturb them. You may need a paperwork or electronic system to record the ongoing condition of your ACMs. You also need to make sure that the system you have put in place to stop uncontrolled work on ACMs continues to be effective. Your employees and anyone else working on your site need to know their responsibilities, what action they should take if they find damaged or deteriorated ACMs, and how to work safely on them. **As long as you have ACMs in your premises, you need to have an effective management plan to minimise exposure to asbestos.**

- **Step 7: Monitor and review the management plan (see paragraphs 85-90).**
  You should review you management plan periodically to make sure that it is still preventing uncontrolled work on ACMs. You also need to be sure that you are continuing to minimise your employees', and others', exposure to asbestos from damaged and deteriorated ACMs. This periodic review of your management plan should typically be done once every six months or where there is a significant change to the structure of the organisation, or personnel responsible for its implementation.

INTRODUCTION

A new duty to manage asbestos in non-domestic premises has been included in the Control of Asbestos at Work Regulations. This requires dutyholders to:

- assess whether premises contain asbestos;

- assess the risk from asbestos; and

- take action to manage the risk from asbestos.

What does this guidance do?

1   Workers in the building and allied trades are exposed to asbestos fibres every time they unknowingly work on building materials that contain asbestos, or carry out work without taking the correct precautions. This exposure can result in the development of asbestos-related diseases, depending on the level, duration and frequency of exposure. This includes minor work, such as installing a new light fitting, through to any major refurbishment or demolition work. Their work can also potentially put others at risk who are in the building.

If you don't manage the asbestos-containing materials in your premises, you could be putting your employees' and other people's health at risk.

2   This guidance tells you how to prevent, or, where this is not reasonably practicable, minimise exposure to this group of workers and other employees by managing the asbestos-containing materials (known as ACMs) on your premises. The guidance contains details on:

- the main factors that determine the risk that ACMs in your premises present to employees and others;

- the immediate steps that should be taken to prevent exposure to asbestos; and

- how to develop a longer term plan to manage the ACMs in your premises.

You don't have to do a survey, but you do have to manage your ACMs.

Introduction

3   This guidance also includes appendices on:

- surveying to find asbestos in buildings;

- how to assess the risks from the asbestos;

- the options available for the management of the ACMs present;

- deciding which management option is appropriate; and

- information on selecting surveyors, consultants and licensed asbestos removal contractors.

4   The guidance also contains case studies to show real examples of approaches to the management of ACMs. There are many ways of managing ACMs in premises and this guidance talks about the range of approaches. But, it is important to realise that there is no one system that fits all. You should use this guidance to help you develop a system that works for you, keeping the two target groups you are trying to protect in mind, that is those exposed:

- during maintenance and building activity on ACMs; and

- during the normal occupancy of the building from damaged and deteriorated ACMs.

Who is this guidance for?

5   This guidance is for those who have a duty to manage the risks from ACMs in premises. This is primarily those who have maintenance and repair responsibilities for the premises through a contract or tenancy. Where there is no contract or tenancy the duty falls to the person in control of the premises. It is also for people who are owners, and sub-lessors of premises which they lease out, managing agents, and others such as architects, surveyors and facilities managers etc, who have a role in the management of premises or who may have relevant information about them. It contains useful guidance for organisations that own and manage rented domestic housing stock such as local authorities and housing associations, who will have to apply the duty to the common parts of housing.

But I'm only a small business, is there a lot I need to do?

6   This guidance expands upon the advice in the free leaflet *A short guide to managing asbestos in premises*.[1] It will be of most use to those in more complex organisations, or those in large, older buildings likely to contain substantial quantities of ACMs who need more detailed guidance.

7   In general, the smaller your business or premises is, the more straightforward the actions you need to take. Managing asbestos in such premises need not always involve major surveys or complex management plans. In fact a few simple steps may be all that is required as long as they are effective in stopping anyone from disturbing asbestos.

For example, the owner of a small retail premises or a farm may find it very simple to comply with their duties under this regulation. They could inspect their buildings them-selves to check the condition of any materials potentially containing asbestos, and if they have no immediate plans to have maintenance work carried out they can presume that the materials contain asbestos without any analysis being made. They would need to repair or, in exceptional cases, remove any damaged materials, either presuming they contain asbestos or checking them first. More serious work (see paragraphs 19 to 23) would have to be done by licensed asbestos contractors, but lower risk work, such as repairs to asbestos cement, can be carried out either by in house staff or a building contractor (provided they work to the standards set out in *Asbestos essentials*[2,3] and HSG 189/1[4]). They would then have to record what they have done.

8   They would then need to make sure that building and maintenance workers, and any other person likely to disturb the material, are warned that it may contain asbestos. Finally, they would need to monitor the condition of the building materials to ensure they do not deteriorate.

9   As the owner or occupier of a small premise, you may not need to read all of this guidance, but you will find parts of it useful. This guidance describes where asbestos is found, its health effects, how we make decisions about the risks to health and so on. Reading this guidance and using it as a reference guide will help you to better appreciate the risks to health and how to control them. It provides advice on selecting contractors and making decisions about repairing and removing asbestos.

Background information for using this guidance

10   This section gives an overview of the guidance, the key principles and how to use it. It covers:

- guidance layout;
- the flow chart;
- risk assessments using algorithms; and
- working with asbestos.

Guidance layout

11   This guidance is long and may seem complex, but with the aid of the simple flow chart on page iv you should find working through the guidance easier. To help you further, the more detailed, specialised parts of the guidance have been put into appendices. The main body of the guidance provides a detailed overview of what you need to do to effectively manage asbestos on your premises. You should read this first part, along with the flow chart, to appreciate what you need to do. The appendices provide detailed guidance on particular aspects of managing asbestos.

12   You may not need to read these appendices straight away. These parts of the guidance were placed at the back of the booklet to be used as reference material when you need to carry out these activities. This allows you to read the guidance and understand the key steps, without having to read all the detail straight away.

A simple flowchart

13   There are only a handful of key steps that you need to understand to manage your ACMs. These are shown in the form of a flow chart on page iv of this guidance. Each step on the flow chart refers to a section of the guidance where you can go to for the detailed guidance. This flow chart should allow you to appreciate, in general terms, what you need to do.

14   Although the flow chart is designed to help your understanding of the key steps, you should be able to satisfy yourself and others that you have understood these steps and fully met your duties under regulation 4 of the Control of Asbestos at Work Regulations 2002 (CAW).[5]

Risk assessments using algorithms

15   The guidance contains algorithms in Appendices 2 and 3, but what are these? They are simple scoring systems to allow you to rate the risks to health from your ACMs. They take into account not only the condition of the asbestos, but the likelihood of people being exposed to the fibres, including during maintenance activities. If you only have a few ACMs on your premises, then decisions about what to do about them may be straightforward. For example, you may decide that only two areas of ACM are a problem due to damage and need some immediate attention. One of them is in an isolated area where nobody works allowing you to simply restrict access to that area in the short term. The other is in an area, such as an office, that needs more urgent attention. Appendix 5 discusses the options open to you.

16   If, however, you have several or even tens or hundreds of locations of ACMs, you need to decide what needs doing first. Budget and time constraints may not allow you to tackle everything straight away, so you need to prioritise them. Algorithms allow you to score each ACM. Those with high scores may need doing first, whereas those with low scores may need no immediate action.

17   There are two algorithms discussed in this guidance. You can find your own approach, but if you choose to use them, then you need both. They are:

● **Material assessment (Appendix 2).**You will see this term referred to throughout the guidance. It is an assessment of the type and condition of your ACMs or presumed ACMs, and their ability to release fibres if disturbed. To do this different aspects are scored. The score for each ACM or presumed ACM will depend on the type of ACM, as some products are more friable (release fibres easier) than others. It also depends on the condition, as the more damaged it is, the more fibres may be released. Any surface treatment and the actual type of asbestos (ie chrysotile (white), amosite (brown), or crocidolite (blue), see paragraph 26) are also considered. Each ACM is scored.

- **Priority assessment (Appendix 3).** This considers the likelihood of the ACM actually being disturbed and exposing your employees or others. For there to be a risk to health it is not enough for it to be damaged and friable, but it also needs to be disturbed and get into the air we breathe. A lump of damaged asbestos in an isolated room which nobody uses, does not present a risk to health. The priority assessment therefore considers the normal occupant activity in that area, the likelihood of disturbance and so on. Each ACM is again scored and these scores are added to those for the material assessment.

Material assessment score for each ACM

+

Priority assessment score for each ACM

=

Risk assessment score for each ACM

then

Rank the risk assessment scores

18   They require you to do nothing more than make a judgment and add the corresponding numbers. The material assessment should be carried out by whoever carries out the survey, as they will have inspected the ACMs. The priority assessment needs to be done with input from the employer who has the knowledge of what takes place in his or her workplace. Once you have your material and priority assessment scores for each ACM, you can add these to get an overall score for each ACM. This process is called your risk assessment for your ACMs. This only provides you with a list of ranked scores for your ACMs, it does not tell you what you have to do. You will then need to decide what action to take, from closing and locking the door to the room containing the damaged ACM, to removing it. Appendix 5 discusses the options.

Algorithms help you assess the risk from your ACMs, they don't tell you what to do with them.

Once you have scored the ACMs, you need to produce an action list for them, which may include leaving in place and managing, removal, repair, monitoring, or simply locking the door to prevent access.

Working with asbestos

19   At some point somebody has to work with ACMs, but who is allowed to do this? The guidance makes reference to good working practices, licensed contractors and so on, but what do you need to do if you have to do some work on an ACM? In the UK work on asbestos has by law to be carried out by a contractor who holds a licence under the Asbestos (Licensing) Regulations 1983 as amended ('the Licensing Regulations'), although there are exceptions. Appendix 6 provides guidance on

selecting a licensed asbestos removal contractor. These Regulations apply to all work on asbestos, *with the exception of:*

- articles made of rubber, plastic, resin or bitumen but which also contain asbestos (eg vinyl floor tiles, electric cables and roofing felts); and

- other asbestos products which may be used at high temperature but have no insulation purposes, such as gaskets, washers, ropes and seals.

20 The Licensing Regulations also do not apply to asbestos cement, defined as material which is mainly a mixture of cement and asbestos and which when in a dry state has a density greater than 1 tonne per cubic metre. This material is typically found as roofing sheets, gutters, cladding, drainpipes and flues.

Figure 2: Asbestos cement: Work with this material does not require a licence

Figure 3: Sprayed asbestos insulation: work with this material requires a licence

Work on asbestos insulation, asbestos insulating board and asbestos coatings can normally only be carried out by licensed contractors. Lower risk work such as that involving asbestos cement can be carried out by maintenance workers, providing they follow good working practices (for example, following the advice in HSE guidance, Asbestos essentials.[2,3])

21 There are also three occasions when you do not need a licence to work on asbestos coating, asbestos insulation and asbestos insulating board (the main products covered by the Licensing Regulations). These are:

- for work of short duration (see paragraph 22);

- for air monitoring or sample collection to identify asbestos; and

- if you are an employer carrying out work with your own employees on your own premises (in this situation the operatives still need to be competent to do the work and 14 days notification of the start of the work should be given to HSE).

22   Work of short duration does not require a licence, providing:

- any one person does not carry out the work for longer than one hour in seven consecutive days; and

- the total time spent on the work by all workers is no more than two hours.

Note that these timings are from the start of the actual set up of the work, to the final clean up, not just the contact with asbestos.

23   These exclusions mean that maintenance workers do not need a licence to do minor work, for example installing a light fitting, providing the work is short duration. But they must follow good working practices. HSE has produced guidance for non-licensed work, *Asbestos essentials.* There are two publications, *an Introduction to asbestos essentials;*[2] and *Asbestos essentials task manual,*[3] both available from HSE Books.

Can I take a sample to see if it contains asbestos?

Appendix 1 provides details about carrying out your own survey work or, if you choose to use an outside organisation to carry out this work, how to go about this. It also contains details about requirements for those analysing samples for the presence of asbestos. But if you simply want to take a sample of a suspect building material to see if it contains asbestos, you can do so. You should do this by:

- making sure you take a representative sample (ie the full depth of the insulation if it is pipework insulation). Take care also that the material may not be asbestos in some places, but asbestos in others;

- taking a small piece, about the size of your thumb nail;

- taking material with the minimal of disturbance. Don't use power tools, saws etc. Look for damaged corners;

- keeping material wet, using a hand-held water spray or similar;

- placing the sample in a bag, placing this bag in another bag and marking it 'may contain asbestos';

- repairing damage with strong adhesive tape or painting with sealant;

- not contaminating surfaces while taking this sample. If there is contamination, use wet wipes to remove it.

If you are unsure, you should employ the services of a competent person (see paragraphs 6-10 of Appendix 1).

What does the law require?

24 There are many health and safety regulations that directly or indirectly place duties on employers in relation to asbestos. The key facts of these regulations are listed below. It is important that you are familiar with these. If you have followed the steps detailed in this guidance in managing your ACMs, you will have taken major steps towards preventing or minimising exposure to asbestos. You will therefore have taken major steps towards complying with your duties under these Regulations.

- The Health and Safety at Work etc Act 1974[6] (HSW Act) requires an employer to conduct their work in such a way that their employees will not be exposed to health and safety risks, and to provide information to other people about their workplace which might affect their health and safety. Section 3 of the HSW Act contains general duties on employers and the self-employed in respect of people other than their own employees. Section 4 contains general duties for anyone who has control, to any extent, over a workplace.

- The Management of Health and Safety at Work Regulations 1999[7] require employers and self-employed people to make an assessment of the risks to the health and safety of themselves, employees, and people not in their employment arising out of or in connection with the conduct of their business - and to make appropriate arrangements for protecting those people's health and safety.

- There are duties to maintain workplace buildings/premises to protect occupants and workers under the Workplace (Health, Safety and Welfare) Regulations 1992.[8]

- The Construction (Design and Management) Regulations 1994[9] require the client to pass on information about the state or condition of any premises (including the presence of hazardous materials such as asbestos) to the planning supervisor before any work begins and to ensure that the health and safety file is available for inspection by any person who needs the information.

- The Control of Asbestos at Work Regulations 2002 (CAW)[5] require employers to prevent the exposure of their employees to asbestos, or where this is not practicable, to reduce the exposure to the lowest possible level. CAW includes a regulation placing a duty on those who have repair and maintenance responsibilities for premises, because of a contract or tenancy, to manage the risk from asbestos in those premises. Where there is no contract or tenancy the person in control will be the duty holder. There is also a duty of cooperation on other parties. The duty is supported by:

  - an Approved Code of Practice[10] and there are two further ACOPs supporting CAW, one directed at licensed work on ACM[11] and one directed at non-licensed work on ACMs[12];

  - this booklet;

- MDHS100 *Surveying, sampling and assessment of asbestos-containing materials*[13]; and

- a free leaflet[1] specifically to give advice to small to medium-sized companies.

Specific legal duties under regulation 4 of CAW 2002

25 The broad requirements on employers and others are to:

- take reasonable steps to find materials likely to contain asbestos;

- presume materials contain asbestos, unless there is strong evidence to suppose they do not;

- assess the risk of the likelihood of anyone being exposed to asbestos from these materials;

- make a written record of the location and the condition of the ACMs and presumed ACMs and keep it up to date;

- repair or remove any material that contains or is presumed to contain asbestos, if necessary, because of the likelihood of disturbance, and its location or condition;

- prepare a plan to manage that risk and put it into effect to ensure that:
  - information on the location and condition of ACMs is given to people who may disturb them during work activities;
  - any material known or presumed to contain asbestos is kept in a good state of repair;

- monitor the condition of ACMs and presumed ACMs; and

- review and monitor the action plan and the arrangements made to put it in place.

The flow chart on page iv of this guidance (Figure 1) outlines the steps required to comply with the duty.

What is asbestos?

Figure 4: Asbestos fibres viewed down a microscope

26   Asbestos is a term used for a number of naturally occurring minerals which have crystallised to form long thin fibres and fibre bundles. The fibres have high tensile strength, and chemical, electrical and heat resistance, and were widely used for these properties; either raw (eg asbestos textiles and insulation packings), or more often, combined with other materials (fireproofings, insulations, boards, asbestos cement sheets etc). There are six regulated types of asbestos, the three main types being - chrysotile, amosite and crocidolite, which were widely imported and used in the UK. These are also referred to as white, brown and blue asbestos respectively. The other three types of regulated asbestos are fibrous actinolite, fibrous tremolite and fibrous anthophyllite, although these were less commonly used.

The health effects of asbestos

27   Although asbestos is a hazardous material, it can only pose a risk to health if the asbestos fibres become airborne and then inhaled. ACMs only release fibres into the air when they are disturbed. If you therefore maintain all your ACMs in good condition, they cannot release fibres and put the health of your workers or others at risk. ACMs are disturbed:

- during any direct action on them, eg drilling, boring, cutting, breaking, smashing, etc;

- during their removal;

- during the demolition of buildings containing them;

- through minimal, but repeated damage, eg an unprotected asbestos insulating board panel on the back of a door which is continually being accidentally knocked or scraped;

- when damaged asbestos, eg damaged pipe insulation or sprayed asbestos on beams/columns, is subject to mechanical vibration and/or strong air currents;

- during any other action that causes the ACM to be disturbed.

Damaged asbestos

28   Some ACMs are more vulnerable to damage and therefore more likely to release fibres than others. If ACMs are not disturbed they are unlikely to release airborne fibres and pose a risk to health.

If ACMs are not disturbed airborne fibres will not be released and therefore they will not pose a risk to health

29   Breathing high concentrations of asbestos fibres can lead to asbestos-related lung diseases, mainly cancers, which kill more people than any other single work-related illness. The disease can take from 15-60 years to develop - so the person who breathes in asbestos fibres will not be immediately aware of a change in their health. There is no cure for asbestos-related diseases.

Asbestos-related diseases kill more people than any other single work-related illness

30   Asbestos-related diseases are currently responsible for up to 3000 deaths a year in the UK. Most of those now dying were exposed to asbestos in the 1950s, 1960s and 1970s when ACMs were widely manufactured and installed. Research undertaken by Professor Julian Peto and HSE epidemiologists in 1995[14] showed that the largest group of workers with asbestos-related diseases were those in construction and the building maintenance trades - such as carpenters, electricians and cable layers. This group accounts for approximately 25% of the current deaths from asbestos-related diseases, as a result of exposures up to 40 years ago. The same group of workers will continue to be at risk if they continue to disturb asbestos unknowingly or without adequate controls.

Figure 5: Maintenance worker, working on asbestos insulating board without adequate controls

The largest group of workers at risk from asbestos-related diseases are those in the building and maintenance trades.

31   The scientific evidence on exactly what fibre concentrations cause disease is unclear. But we do know that the more asbestos dust inhaled the greater the risk to health.

32   While maintenance workers are the main group at risk from asbestos fibres released when ACMs are disturbed during maintenance, fibres could also be released as a result of other types of disturbance and be breathed in by employees and others present in the building.

> **Can a single exposure give an asbestos-related disease?**
>
> **All exposures to asbestos should be avoided, however, that does not mean that you should necessarily worry about a one-off exposure. From time to time, accidental exposures to asbestos may occur and can be a cause of much concern and distress to the individuals concerned. Your risk of developing an asbestos-related disease depends how much asbestos you are exposed to, for how long and on how many different occasions. A one-off short-term exposure is unlikely to be of concern, but each time you are exposed, the risk increases a little bit more. Think of this like smoking. The more times you smoke, the greater your risk of developing cancer. See paragraph 84 on awareness training for your employees and others.**

Where in premises can asbestos be found and what does it look like?

33   Asbestos has been incorporated into many materials over the last century. A drawing of a building showing many of the uses to which ACMs have been put is shown in Figure 6. This diagram does not show all the possible uses for ACMs.

34   The commercial use of asbestos in the UK began around the end of the nine-teenth century and increased gradually until World War II. Immediately after World War II, large quantities of asbestos were used, particularly for new 'system-built' buildings in the 1950s, 1960s and early 1970s. ACMs were also routinely used in the refurbishment of older buildings.

Asbestos locations

35   Asbestos has been the subject of gradual voluntary and formal bans since 1969, for example:

• 	the use of blue asbestos stopped almost completely in about 1970;

• 	the installation of sprayed coatings decreased gradually from 1970 to 1980 and was the subject of a legal ban from 1985;

- the installation of asbestos insulating board decreased sharply after 1980 and stopped completely in 1985;

- the use of asbestos paints and varnishes stopped in about 1988;

- the installation of asbestos-containing decorative plasters was legally banned in 1992;

- the installation of asbestos cement was prohibited in 1999.

36   By 1999 the importation, supply and use of all forms of ACMs had been banned, with the exception of a few specialised applications.

Take care, these dates are only provided as a guideline, as asbestos held in stock may have been used after these dates.

Figure 6: Asbestos building (see pages 14 and 15)

KEY

ROOF AND EXTERIOR WALLS

1. Roof sheets and tiles
2. Guttering and drainpipe
3. Wall cladding
4. Soffit/facia boards
5. Panel beneath window
6. Roofing felt and coating to metal wall cladding

BOILER, VESSELS AND PIPEWORK

7. Lagging on boiler, pipework, calorifier etc.
8. Damaged lagging and associated debris
9. Paper lining under non-asbestos pipe lagging
10. Gasket in pipe and vessel joints
11. Rope seal on boiler access hatch and between cast iron boiler sections
12. Paper lining inside steel boiler casing
13. Boiler flue

CEILINGS

14. Spray coating to ceiling, walls, beams/columns
15. Loose asbestos in ceiling/floor cavity
16. Tiles, slats, canopies and firebreaks above ceilings
17. Textured coatings and paints

INTERIOR WALLS/PANELS

18. Loose asbestos inside partition walls
19. Partition walls
20. Panel beneath window
21. Panel lining to lift shaft
22. Panelling to vertical and horizontal beams
23. Panel behind electrical equipment
24. Panel on access hatch to service riser
25. Panel lining service riser and floor
26. Heater cupboard around domestic boiler
27. Panel behind/under heater
28. Panel on or inside, fire door
29. Bath panel

FLOORING MATERIALS

30. Floor tiles, linoleum and paper backing, lining to suspended floor

AIR HANDLING SYSTEMS

31. Lagging
32. Gaskets
33. Anti-vibration gaiter

DOMESTIC APPLIANCES

34. Gaskets, rope seals and panels in domestic boilers
35. 'Caposil' insulating blocks, panels, paper, string etc in domestic heater
36. String seals on radiators

OTHER

37. Fire blanket
38. Water tank
39. Brake/clutch lining

ASBESTOS BUILDING

TYPICAL LOCATIONS FOR THE MOST COMMON ASBESTOS-CONTAINING MATERIALS

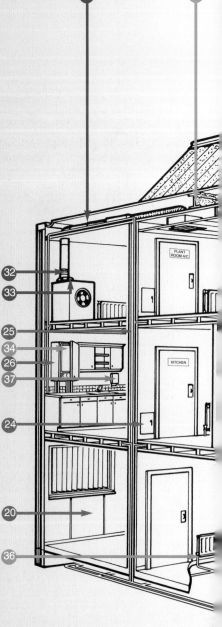

Note: This diagram does not show all possible uses and locations of asbestos-containing materials. A detailed survey will be required to identify all asbestos-containing materials present in a building.

Further information can be found in the HSE publication MDHS100 *Surveying and sampling asbestos-containing material* [13]

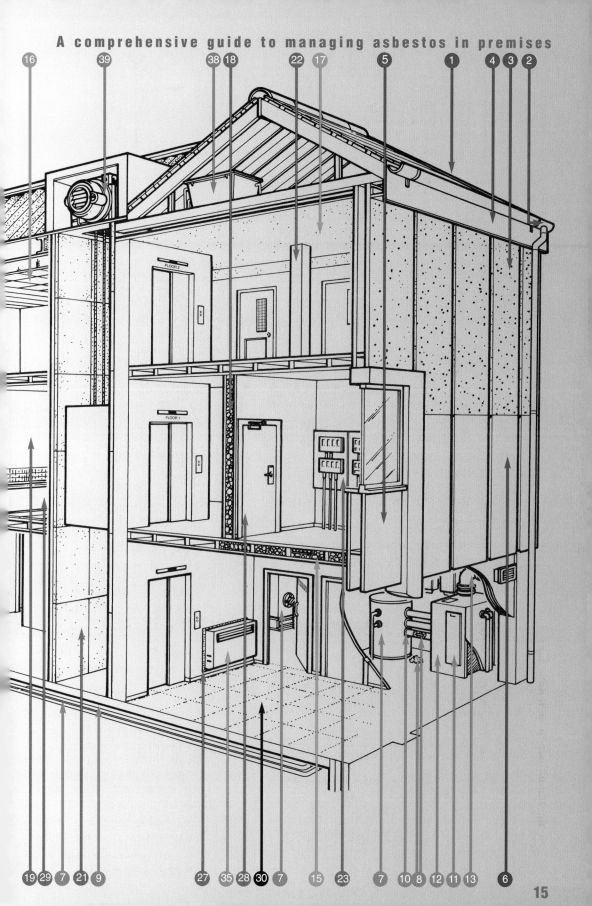

DEVELOPING AN ASBESTOS MANAGEMENT STRATEGY

37   The purpose of a management strategy is to prevent exposure to airborne asbestos now and for the duration of the time ACMs are present on your premises. The group most likely to be exposed are maintenance workers and others working on the fabric of a building. However, there are others who may disturb asbestos accidentally who may also be at risk. Employees carrying out their everyday duties may accidentally walk through asbestos debris or damage ACMs (eg a chair or trolley knocking an asbestos panel on the back of a door). You should consider what you need to do now and what you need to do in the longer term. This part of the guidance follows the steps in the flow chart on page iv.

Who should manage the ACMs on my premises?

38   To make sure that ACMs within your premises are properly managed, you will need to identify the person within your organisation who will be responsible for that management. The responsible person will need the resources, skills, training, authority etc to ensure the job can be done. The right person for this role will vary from one organisation to another, depending on the size of the organisation, its structure, and the roles and the responsibilities of the personnel within it. For small companies, it is likely to be the owner; for other organisations where the role will be more involved the safety officer, occupational hygienist or safety, health and environment manager may be the appropriate person; for others the maintenance or estates manager or the building or facility manager will be more suitable.

Immediate actions (Steps 1-3)

Step 1: Confirm what you already know about the ACMs on your premises, and review how you are currently managing them

39   You should first consider whether there are likely to be ACMs on your premises. If you are sure that you don't have any ACMs then you need not go any further. For example, if you have already done a survey/inspection which identifies them and you also have records that they have been removed. Your building may never have contained asbestos if, for example, it was constructed after 1999. You should make a record of this to confirm to others

Developing an asbestos management strategy

that you have made your assessment under regulation 4 and concluded that you do not have ACMs on your premises. Paragraphs 33-36 provide information on the approximate dates when the installation of different asbestos products ceased in the UK. Don't rely on these dates as they are only approximate and asbestos held in stock may have been used after these dates. More recent developments are extremely unlikely to contain asbestos, eg post-1999 buildings, which you may be able to confirm with architects, planners or the builders.

40   If you know your premises contain asbestos or are unsure then you will need to assess your current management of ACMs. Find out what you do already. You will need that information to decide which of the next steps are appropriate. This will help you to decide how much you need to do, if anything, to manage your ACMs. In carrying out this assessment, you should ask yourself the following questions:

- Is all maintenance/building/demolition work controlled, so that nobody can unknowingly work on ACMs? Any maintenance or building work can damage and disturb asbestos, such as drilling through panels to fit new wiring, crawling through roof spaces, etc. Who controls this work and is there a system in place to make sure that the content of any materials that have to be disturbed is known or can be quickly determined from records or through analysis?

- Do maintenance/building trades know how to work safely on ACMs? Do they know when they are allowed to work on ACMs (see paragraphs 19-23)? It is not simply good enough to know where ACMs are, but workers need to be trained to work safely on them. Measures need to be in place to ensure the release of fibres is minimised, such as wetting and the use of shadow vacuuming.

- Do you know the condition of all your ACMs or materials presumed to contain asbestos? Most importantly you should know if there are any damaged materials on your premises that may contain asbestos.

- Have all damaged and deteriorated ACMs been repaired, removed or isolated so that nobody can be exposed to fibres released from them?

- Is there a management plan in place for recording findings in relation to the ACMs on your premises and monitoring their condition?

- Does everyone know their roles and responsibilities for the management of ACMs on your premises?

41   You may have answered 'yes' to some of these and 'no' to others, or you may not be sure. Reading this guidance will help you to decide what more you need to do. But there are many ways to effectively manage ACMs. Use this guidance to help you decide what approach best suits the needs of your business. The following steps will give you an introduction to managing ACMs.

Step 2: Prevent work on premises that may disturb the fabric of the building until measures to control the risk have been implemented

Prevent work that will disturb the fabric of the building until the presence or absence of ACMs has been established.

42   Can your employees or others carry out maintenance or building work on your premises without first checking whether they are working on ACMs? To answer 'no' you would need to be sure that there is a system in place ensuring that paper or electronic records are looked at first, or that the building materials are checked to see whether they contain asbestos. If no such measures are in place or you are unsure, then you should put measures in place to prevent disturbance to ACMs or presumed ACMs or ensure appropriate precautions are taken when working on the materials. The most effective way to do this is to prevent work that will disturb the fabric of the building until the presence or absence of ACMs has been established and any necessary precautionary measures taken.

43   Whichever method is used to control maintenance workers and contractors, the objective is that it should be effective in preventing them or anyone else from being unknowingly exposed to airborne asbestos fibres.

44   You should do this immediately. You do not need to wait until you have decided whether you are going to do an inspection or a survey and what type of survey you will do. Any work, irrespective of how minor should be regarded as having the potential to expose someone to asbestos. Uncontrolled disturbances, such as drilling holes, can create high levels of asbestos fibres.

45   Once you have stopped the work, you then need to decide how you are going to control it. This should include:

● what system you are going to instigate to control all maintenance and building work, for example, permit-to-work systems (see paragraph 82-83);

● who is going to be in charge of overseeing this system;

● when ACMs are found, who will work on them and what methods will they use (see paragraphs 19-23);

● what training and information is going to be given to maintenance and building trades, as well as the occupants of the building (see paragraph 84).

46   In the long term your knowledge of the location of ACMs on your premises is likely to increase as surveys are carried out (Step 4 talks about long-term options). When an area has been refurbished you are also likely to know far more about the building materials that were previously used in that location, and you may have had some ACMs removed.

Step 3: Carry out an initial inspection for damage and disturbance of materials and take immediate action to control these

This is not a survey, but an inspection for building materials that are damaged, or could be easily disturbed to release fibres.

47   Have you assessed whether there is any substantial damage or deterioration to the fabric of the building? To answer 'yes' to this you must be sure that all building materials or at least those that could contain asbestos are in reasonable condition. If you are unsure, then you should inspect your premises for damaged materials that may contain asbestos. Workers may be exposed to asbestos generated into the air they breathe, if they disturb them. This is an immediate action because you want to stop your employees from being exposed to asbestos *now*. In Step 2 you stopped uncontrolled work on the fabric of the building, but now you need to make sure there are no damaged ACMs on your premises. This simply means walking around your premises and looking for any major damage. This is not a survey, as you are not specifically looking for ACMs. You are looking for materials that are damaged and that may be disturbed by your employees and others. Clearly this doesn't require a knowledge of what asbestos looks like or where it is found, but simply what damage looks like. Major damage includes the delamination and erosion of sprayed coatings and thermal insulation, significant damage to insulating boards, which has resulted in the release of debris or signs of repeated and frequent surface damage. You may find:

Figure 7: Asbestos insulating board wall panels badly damaged

- significant damage, such as:

  - holes in wall panels;

  - pipework insulation hanging off;

  - spray insulation hanging off; and

  - loose debris on the floor, in roof voids, dry risers etc.

48   If you find any major damage, you should then consider whether they contain asbestos. If they obviously do not, for example, glass, wood or plastic then you can take action as you see fit. If, however, they may contain asbestos, or you are not sure, then you may need to take action to repair the damage, remove the ACM or to make sure that workers do not disturb it. You may wish to arrange for a sample to be taken for analysis to confirm that the damaged material contains asbestos before carrying out remedial work.

49   If it is not possible to immediately remove or repair the ACM, then you could isolate it until remedial action can be taken. You could simply lock the room, place a warning notice on the door 'do not enter, damaged asbestos present, contact: A.N.Other on 12345678', until you can take action to repair or remove the damaged asbestos. Remember, if asbestos is left undisturbed, even if in poor condition, it will not release fibres into the air we breathe. For example unoccupied areas need not be subject to Steps 1 to 3 if the asbestos is safely locked away.

50   When you have completed this inspection, you may have a list of materials that require some action. It is important that you remember that it is not the ACM in the poorest condition that needs tackling first, but the one that is most likely to expose someone to asbestos fibres. A large amount of asbestos debris on the floor may in some circumstances present a lower risk to health than a panel on the back of a door. If the panel is constantly being damaged, causing it to release fibres, it may be exposing those nearby. Whereas the large pile of asbestos debris may be in a room that nobody goes in.

51   This damage and disturbance inspection may not take very long if your premises are small, but if you are in control of a large building or many buildings, it could take several weeks to complete. You may therefore need to plan this damage and disturbance inspection.

52   Completing your damage and disturbance inspection may become part of your strategy for managing ACMs (see Step 4), particularly if your premises are large or complex. You might want to look for any materials that may contain asbestos as part of this step, not just those that are damaged ie combine this step with the requirement to make your full assessment as to whether ACMs are on the premises.

53   There may be short cuts you can take to speed this inspection up. You may have hundreds of premises in your control. You could ask those in control of each building to inform you of any building materials that are significantly damaged and/or materials that contain asbestos where this is known. You may decide to do those buildings most occupied first. There may be buildings that you very rarely enter which you can delay inspecting, possibly never inspecting them until you have to go in them.

54   Remember, this is not necessarily a survey, this is only an inspection for damage and disturbance. Unless you choose to carry out the material assessment (see Step 4) at the same time, a full assessment will have to be made as a separate action.

55   Once you have identified the major damage you can assess the risk to health (see Appendices 2 and 3) and take the appropriate action (see Appendix 5).

Continuing actions (Steps 4-7)

Step 4: Develop a strategy for compliance

56   Your immediate actions should have stopped people from the building trades from unknowingly working on ACMs and you should now have a system in place to make sure that these are worked on safely. You should know where all your damaged and deteriorated materials are, or at least the significant damage, and should have put in place plans to carry out urgent repairs.

57   You now need to plan a comprehensive strategy to ensure that you manage the long-term risks from asbestos in your premises. In other words: How can your organisation, with its mix of building types, best comply with its duty under the Regulations?

58   The first stage of this process will be to decide what needs to be done (if anything) to complete the inspection and assessment of materials which could contain asbestos on your premises. As well as identifying whether materials contain asbestos, this should ensure that the condition of all such materials is assessed to detect any damage (from minor scrapes and scratches to loose debris from insulation in dry risers).

59 In deciding how best to carry out the assessment required by the Regulations, you should bear in mind that there are three options:

- after excluding materials such as glass, brick and wood, you can presume that all other materials contain asbestos, and record them as such;

- you can determine, by sampling and analysis, whether the material contains asbestos;

- you can establish, using other **very strong** evidence (eg building records), that the material or a building does not contain asbestos. Note: this evidence must be accurate beyond all reasonable doubt.

60   If you presume materials contain asbestos you must consequently use appropriate work methods and contractors when disturbing the fabric of the building. Although this will save on analytical costs, you may be spending money on more expensive working methods if materials don't contain asbestos. **If the work is minor (see paragraph 22) and will only take a few minutes, you could assume it contains asbestos and follow the proper precautions. This may be preferable to waiting for the results of analysis.** Alternatively, prior to work on a presumed ACM, take samples and have them analysed to confirm or refute the presence of asbestos. The results will determine the work methods and contractors required to carry out the work. Page 7 tells you how to take samples safely.

61   There are advantages and disadvantages to this approach, which will depend on the size and complexity of your premises. Whatever your approach, you will have to find out at some point whether the material contains asbestos (now or before any work takes place on it). You could assume that everything contains asbestos and take the appropriate actions without ever knowing whether it contains asbestos. This is likely to be a costly option as you would be taking relatively more expensive options for materials that may be free of asbestos.

62   Alternatively, you may decide that this is too difficult to control, that the extensive nature of maintenance and building work means that you will be constantly holding up the work to find out if asbestos is present. You may therefore decide that you want to fully survey your premises and determine the location of your ACMs. This then becomes an integral part of your management system. It may be that employees and contractors will be able to access electronic or paper records to determine if the material they are about to work on contains asbestos. The Approved Code of Practice gives more information on these issues.

63   It may take you some time to survey every part of your premises. Simply employing the services of a competent surveyor (see Appendix 1, paragraph 6) to start at one end of your site, surveying every building and area may be unrealistic. You may have many sites, possibly hundreds or even thousands. You therefore need to have a system that works for you, which may be a combination of the above approaches.

64   You may be able to categorise all your buildings/areas, which may help you to develop a strategy for approaching surveys. This might break down along the lines of the following:

- The age of the building or when it was last refurbished. The more modern the building or if it has been extensively refurbished in recent years, the less likely it is that it contains ACMs.

- The occupancy of the building. You may decide that those buildings with the greatest occupancy should be looked at first, or you may be in control of schools and decide that these should be looked at first. You may have buildings, such as rarely used storerooms or substations, that are rarely accessed.

- The type of activity. The activities in some areas may be more likely to damage ACMs, such as corridors which frequently have trolleys pushed down them, or factories with fork-lift truck movement, or buildings where maintenance work is carried out more frequently. The condition of services in some buildings may dictate frequent repair work.

- Future plans for rooms/buildings. If you are planning refurbishment in a particular area you may decide that this should be given priority.

65   You will need to gather together and consider all the information that can be obtained about the premises such as building plans that will help you to establish if asbestos is present. This includes the age of the building, anything that tells you what materials were used during construction or any subsequent refurbishment/maintenance

of the premises and any information which shows that asbestos materials have been removed. You will need to consider how accurate all this information is and check this during any survey.

Types of survey

66   More detailed inspections, usually called surveys, are described in MDHS100.[13] The document sets out three different types of survey.

- Type 1 surveys are known as presumptive surveys where no sampling is carried out. There is no positive identification of ACMs; instead any material which can be reasonably expected to contain asbestos must be presumed to do so, and its condition assessed (Appendix 2). For this type of survey you can only exclude materials from your list of 'presumed asbestos' if you are completely confident that they do not contain asbestos, for example, glass, metal or wood (although asbestos may be hidden by them). If you are having a survey carried out you may therefore decide that a Type 1 would not be that beneficial as you would still be uncertain about the location of your ACMs. You may decide that you should go to the extra expense of a Type 2, but there may be reasons why a Type 1 is enough for your needs.

- Type 2 surveys are known as sampling surveys. Samples of suspected ACMs are collected and analysed to confirm or refute the suspected presence of asbestos. Again, the ACM's condition must be assessed.

- Type 3 surveys are carried out before major refurbishment or demolition. This survey may involve destructive inspection to gain access to all areas. This type of survey is designed to be used as a basis for tendering for the removal of ACMs from the building before demolition so the survey does not assess the condition of the asbestos.

Figure 8: Carrying out a Type 1 survey

Figure 9: Taking a sample with a corer for a Type 2/3 survey

Figure 10: Removing panels to gain complete access for a Type 3 survey

67   Within any premises there may be several buildings to be assessed and different types of surveys/inspections may be required for each building or even parts of buildings, depending on the current or future use of those buildings. For example there may be a building which is due for a major refurbishment (ie it involves partial demolition or removal of major parts of the fabric of the building) and so will require a Type 3 survey. Another may be a modern building, built around 1995, in which it is unlikely that any ACM was used. If it is unlikely that ACMs exist in the building, and building specifications are available to support this view, a Type 1 survey may be sufficient until work is required on the building. Then sampling of any presumed ACMs will be required, unless a decision is taken to treat the material as if it were an ACM. Alternatively, it may be that the ACMs in an older building have already been identified so further sampling is not necessary, so a Type 1 survey will be sufficient to complete the material assessment.

Setting priorities for surveys

68   In addition to deciding on the type of inspection or survey required for each building or part of building, priorities for surveying will need to be established. These priorities may be influenced by several factors:

- the number of buildings on the premises;

- the age of the buildings;

- the dates of previous refurbishments;

- the occupancy of the buildings, including the frequency of visitors;

- the activities occurring within the buildings;

- the results of previous surveys/knowledge of previous asbestos removal work; and

- the likelihood of maintenance work/refurbishment being required.

69   Once the priorities have been set, these should be recorded with the reasons why and a programme of surveys drawn up. The programme should be reviewed on a regular basis, as priorities may change over time.

70   Once the survey strategy has been defined, a decision will be required on who will carry out the survey(s). This decision may be influenced by a number of factors which are discussed in Appendix 1.

Survey reports

71   Where a survey has been carried out, the survey report will form the basis upon which your organisation will develop its management plan. The report should contain the following about each ACM or presumed ACM:

- location (including accessibility);

- quantity;

- extent;

- condition;

- product type;

- type of asbestos (or presume it is crocidolite (blue asbestos) since this is the most hazardous type); and

- a material assessment.

Appendix 2 has more details about report content.

72   Consider the format of the survey report. For all but the simplest of surveys, a computer database will enable the records to be kept up to date and readily accessible. Other factors which need to be considered are:

- long-term storage of records;

- accessibility of information to those who need it; and

- use of photographs/drawings/plans.

73   The options available for recording the survey include:

- paper copy;

- PC-based electronic copy;

- survey on organisation's intranet; and/or

- survey registered on an Internet site managed by a third party.

74   These options are discussed in greater detail in Appendix 1.

Step 5: Carry out a risk assessment of your ACMs to set priorities for management

Producing a risk assessment

75   If you have carried out an inspection or a survey, you will need to risk assess each of the ACMs or presumed ACMs identified. These risk assessments help you decide what action is appropriate to deal with the ACMs and to make decisions on what needs to be tackled first. If you have found several ACMs in poor condition, it may not be possible to tackle them all at once. The procedure outlined below is more likely to be used following completion of a survey, however, it can similarly be used after a damage and disturbance inspection. The risk assessments are carried out in two stages.

It is not simply whether the ACM will release fibres, but if people are exposed to those fibres once disturbed, that determines the risk to health.

- **The material assessment (Appendix 2).** This is an assessment of the condition of the material and the likelihood of it releasing fibres on disturbance. The report prepared by the surveyor (if you have had a survey carried out) should include this. The material assessment is discussed in detail in MDHS100[13] and in Appendix 2. The material assessment will give a good initial guide to the priority for management as it will identify the materials which will most readily release airborne fibres if disturbed. However, this may not always indicate high priority for remedial action.

- **Priority assessment (Appendix 3).** Management priority must be determined by carrying out an assessment of the likelihood of the ACMs being disturbed. Remember even an ACM in the poorest condition only presents a risk to health if the fibres are in the air we breathe. This priority assessment takes into account factors such as:

    - maintenance activities (include cleaning if appropriate);

    - likelihood of disturbance;

    - human exposure potential; and

    - occupant activity or those visitors to the building.

76   The risk assessment takes into account the results of the material assessment in addition to the factors listed above. The purpose of the risk assessment is to indicate priorities for action. These priorities can then be used to develop the action plan. A number of worked examples are given in Appendix 4 to illustrate its use.

The risk assessment includes a material assessment and a priority assessment.

The material assessment looks at the type and condition of the ACM and the ease with which it will release fibres if disturbed.

The priority assessment looks at the likelihood of someone disturbing the ACM.

77   These algorithms on first consideration may appear daunting. Look at the examples given and try using them yourself for likely ACMs present in your premises. They are relatively straightforward to use once you have got used to them. But these are only provided as guidance, you can use any other approach to setting your own

priorities, providing it considers your ACMs in terms of their potential to expose your employees and others to asbestos.

Step 6: Develop a long-term management plan

Developing a management plan

78   Once the risk assessments have been carried out for each ACM, these are then used in the development of the management plan. If an algorithm has been used in the risk assessment process then the scores for each material can be used to give priority to those materials needing action. The next stage is to decide what actions to take. Do you leave the ACM in place and manage it? Do you repair or remove the ACM? There are a number of options available and these are discussed in detail in Appendix 5. Appendix 5 also has a number of flow charts which will help you choose the most appropriate option.

79   The way these decisions are made will vary from one organisation to another. For an employer with a single building with a small number of different ACMs, the decisions should be straightforward. They will be made on the basis of the risk assessment, the type of material and the likelihood of it being damaged, future plans for refurbishment, and the practicality of the various options. Priorities can be set, with target timescales for completion.

80   For larger organisations the decisions taken about management options are likely to be more complex. For example, hospital complexes or local authority building stock may have a wide range of building types, including domestic housing, schools, municipal buildings and commercial premises. In these cases it is more likely that decisions are made on a generic basis, taking one type of building at a time; schools for example may be given priority as the potential for exposure at an early age is higher. Large chemical complexes will also have to take into account other major hazards, plant shutdown and maintenance programmes in addition to controlling the risks from each ACM as identified by the risk assessment. The case studies demonstrate how four different organisations are managing their ACMs.

Contents of a management plan

81   The management plan should be clear and unambiguous. It should set out the aims of the plan, what is going to be done, when it is going to be done, and how it is going to be done. There needs to be clear lines of responsibility, with each person involved understanding their role. A mechanism for regular monitoring and an annual review of the management plan to ensure that it is working properly should also be included. The type of information which should be included in a management plan is listed below:

- the details of how the location and condition of known or presumed ACMs is recorded;

- priority assessments including priority assessment scores if algorithms have been used;

- a table of priority for action;

- decisions about management options including the rationale (this may include reference to the flow charts in Appendix 5);

- a timetable for action;

- monitoring arrangements;

- employees and their responsibilities;

- training arrangements for employees and contractors;

- a plan of implementation of new procedures, including those for external contractors;

- the mechanisms for passing information about the location and condition of ACMs to those who need it;

- who will oversee the quality of the entries made on the management plan; and

- a procedure for review of the plan, including a timetable.

Appendix 5 contains details about management options and includes flow charts which help in their selection.

Appendix 6 contains details about selecting contractors, managing asbestos removal/repair contracts, and selecting consultants/laboratories.

Controlling work on the fabric of your building

82   You need to have a system in place to control any maintenance or building work on the fabric of your building. This may take one of several forms, depending on the size and complexity of the organisation, for example:

- in a small organisation, one person can be nominated to control all work carried out by in-house maintenance workers and all contractors;

- limit the number of contractors who work on your premises to one or two who are familiar with the buildings and procedures in use in your organisation;

- the maintenance or safety department may be charged with ensuring that information regarding the presence of ACMs or presumed ACMs is passed on to contractors who come onto your premises;

- a formal, written safe system of work incorporating permits-to-work may be used to control maintenance workers and contractors alike. This is most likely to be necessary in larger organisations where it is difficult for one person to maintain control over the number of contractors on site. It provides a framework for those controlling the contractors.

83   Whichever method is used to control maintenance workers and contractors, the objective is that it should be effective in preventing them from being unknowingly exposed to airborne asbestos, or exposing others nearby.

Awareness/training for employees, contractors and others

84   There are different types of training that you may need to provide to your employees and others. You should aim to have an open and responsive culture where employees are not afraid of asbestos and know how it is managed in their place of work. Your training could include the following elements.

All staff

● The health risks associated with asbestos, taking care to provide the right balance. You want everyone to respect asbestos, but not to fear it. Asbestos is an extremely emotive subject, and often the simple knowledge of its presence is enough to make employees afraid of being in the same room. This has often resulted in poor decisions being made about remedial action when it is found. They should be informed:

  - that you can only be exposed to asbestos if you disturb the fibres into the air you breathe;

  - that asbestos in good condition should be left in place;

  - that any exposure to asbestos should be avoided and that the risk increases as the level, duration and frequency of exposure increases;
  - that the increased risk to health from a one-off accidental exposure is negligible and not a cause for concern;

  - what to do if they find asbestos or a damaged material, which they think could contain asbestos;

  - what to expect from maintenance employees and building operatives.

Maintenance and building operatives

Maintenance and building operatives should be informed:

● of the points listed above for 'all staff';

● what asbestos products are and where you are likely to find them;

● that they should never work on any building material without first knowing whether it contains asbestos;

● of the procedure to follow before starting any work where building materials are to be disturbed;

● of the safe working methods for working on ACMs;

- what work they can and cannot do on ACMs.

Those with specific responsibilities

- You may also want to provide additional training for those in control of parts of the management plan, or those who have specific responsibilities such as supervising and controlling maintenance or building work, or those carrying out inspections or surveys.

Step 7: Monitor and review the management plan

85   Once the management plan has been made and recorded, the implementation of the plan needs to be addressed. Getting as far as the development of the management plan can be a time-consuming and in some cases costly business, but unless the management plan continues to be a living process the resources used to develop it will have been wasted.

86   Consider the following when making arrangements for the implementation and ongoing maintenance of the management plan:

- monitoring the action plan to make sure that all remedial work has been adequately carried out;

- monitoring of ACMs or presumed ACMs left in position;

- frequency of monitoring of ACMs/presumed ACMs;

- updating the asbestos record following repair/removal of ACMs;

- ongoing communication/training of maintenance workers/contractors;

- continued awareness amongst all employees;

- monitoring of the implementation timetable; and

- lessons learned following incidents and accidents involving ACMs.

87   The management plan should be subject to at least a six monthly thorough review. This should critically review all the management processes and their effectiveness as well as the overall progress made against the implementation timetable. For example, you should find out:

- if the plan is referred to in safe systems of work procedures;

- how the plan is communicated to maintenance workers, others working in the vicinity of asbestos, and external contractors;

- if the plan is referred to in specifications for tenders, where appropriate;

- if emergency plans/contingency procedures refer to the management plan; and

- if local emergency services are aware of the presence of asbestos in the buildings.

88   There may be changes to the structure of the organisation, or personnel changes which will require changes to the management plan. When reviewing the management plan, the list below gives guidance about some of the issues you might consider:

- Effectiveness of current management plan:

  - in preventing exposure;

  - in controlling maintenance workers/contractors;

  - in highlighting the need for action to repair/remove ACMs;

  - in raising awareness among all employees.

- Issues which may affect the management plan, including:

  - changes to the organisational structure and/or staff;

  - resourcing the management plan;

  - changes to company procedures; and

  - changes in building use/occupancy/refurbishment plans.

- Instances of failure of the procedures, for example:

  - where procedures have not been followed and why not;

  - where procedures have been inadequate and why;

  - where exposure to airborne asbestos fibres has occurred.

89   It must not be forgotten that the objective of the management plan is to reduce the risk of exposure and the consequential potential ill-health. If it can be demonstrated that exposure is under control, the management plan will be doing its intended job.

90   Table 1 indicates some common errors relating to asbestos management, highlighting the potential consequences and proposed solutions. It is by no means exhaustive, but is included here to illustrate where asbestos management has gone wrong in the past, and help to prevent these common mistakes in the future.

Table 1 Some common errors and outcomes in asbestos management with some solutions

Common error	Outcome	Possible solutions
Not all ACMs are identified	People may work on an ACM exposing themselves and others, perhaps significantly	A thorough survey
ACM is identified as unlikely to release asbestos fibres when it could do so (because of its type or state)	Potential release of airborne fibres underestimated	Consult guidance and/or trained personnel
ACM is identified as likely to release asbestos fibres when this is unlikely	Unnecessary and costly action may be taken to prevent an insignificant risk People's concerns and worries may be raised unnecessarily Maintenance and other work may be unnecessarily disrupted	Consult guidance and/or trained personnel
Poor liaison and discussion between surveyor and premises manager or owner	(1) ACM is missed; or (2) Potential disturbance is underestimated and therefore not taken into account by the surveyor (Result - potential risk is underestimated); or (3) Potential disturbance is overestimated by the surveyor when, in fact, it is unlikely (Result - potential risk is overestimated).	Make sure liaison and communications between yourself and the surveyor are clear and appropriately detailed Develop the final risk assessment together as you know the type and level of occupancy of your premises
ACM identified but presence not communicated effectively to contractors or maintenance personnel	ACM is disturbed possibly resulting in significant exposure	Make sure liaison and communications between yourself and the contractor or maintenance personnel is clear and effective
People become concerned because of the presence of an ACM, even though in good condition	Unnecessary and costly action may be taken to prevent an insignificant risk People's concerns and worries may be raised unnecessarily Maintenance and other work may be unnecessarily disrupted	Consult guidance and or trained personnel

continued overleaf

Common error	Outcome	Possible solutions
People do not appreciate how energetic work (eg drilling, hammering etc) near damaged ACM may release airborne fibres	People may work close to the ACM exposing themselves and others, perhaps significantly	All maintenance and other workers should receive training and instruction as should supervisors
People work on or near ACM but don't follow the correct procedures	People may expose themselves and others, perhaps significantly	Follow HSE's *Asbestos essentials* task guidance sheets or other good practice guidance (see paragraphs 19 to 23)
Labels obscured or not easily visible	People may be exposed and/or expose others	Make labelling policy clear and inspect labels on a regular basis
Location plan used names of people or other transient identifying factors	Locations of asbestos no longer known	Use room numbers or other permanent identifying factors
Complete a survey but do nothing else	People may be exposed and/or expose others	Inform others of survey findings and develop management plan
Maintenance staff work on ACM inadvertently	Maintenance staff exposed	Maintenance operatives should be given basic training on what they should do before working on the fabric of the building

CASE STUDY 1: LOCAL AUTHORITY: LONDON BOROUGH OF ISLINGTON

The scale of the task

The London Borough of Islington has approximately:

- 35 000 properties under its control, of which around 32 000 are domestic and the responsibility of the council's housing services;

- over 5000 employees;

- more than 600 contractors on a prescribed list of tenderers, and the council works in partnership with numerous management organisations.

Premises include:

- public buildings, such as leisure centres and libraries;

- education buildings, such as schools and nurseries;

- social services buildings, including day care centres and residential homes;

- operational buildings, such as depots and workshops;

- administration buildings.

The council also owns a range of properties such as shops, restaurants and offices, which they commercially lease, often to the voluntary sector. In contrast, the council often leases properties from third parties, which are used by council employees. This situation is complex, but by no means unusual for a local authority.

There has, over the years, been much surveying of buildings for asbestos, and a substantial amount of removal of asbestos, particularly in housing services. Reports and records from the asbestos surveys were kept and entered onto a computerised asbestos database.

In housing services it had become a standard practice to survey domestic properties for asbestos whenever they became void. As no effective use was being made of the information held on the Corporate Asbestos Database (CAD), some properties had been

CASE STUDY 1

surveyed more than once over the years, while other blocks were not surveyed as properties were not becoming void.

It was clear that systems and procedures needed updating, to ensure that information held on the Corporate Asbestos Database was effectively used.

A new strategy

A review of housing services asbestos policy was originally driven by the necessity to reduce the void turnaround time. However, when HSE proposals for a new 'duty to manage' asbestos were published, a strategy for management of asbestos was drawn up based on the Consultative Document published by the Health and Safety Commission.

It was very clear from the outset that the council's housing services could not immediately survey all of the 32 000 properties under its control. A management strategy had to be developed to provide protection to those working on, and in, the buildings, while allowing the day-to-day work of the service to continue.

Housing services' action

- A new asbestos policy based upon the management of asbestos rather than wholesale removal was developed in consultation with the CAD co-ordinator.

- Key staff who controlled maintenance work in premises were trained to P405 (BIOH management of asbestos module).

- The asbestos management system required information to be requested from the corporate asbestos database prior to commissioning works.

- An audit trail system was developed and implemented to ensure that records on CAD were updated with all relevant information from the initial request to the completion of works.

- A strategy for surveying the 32 000 properties was developed based upon an initial target to conduct Type 2 surveys in 10% of housing blocks.

A Corporate Asbestos Database

CAD has been critical to the success of housing services' asbestos management system. The database was developed in-house using commercially available database software. It is compatible with the CAD system used by the council's architectural and surveying service, so that floor plans indicating the location of ACMs can be downloaded from the system for maintenance workers, when they are carrying out work on housing properties.

CAD manages and maintains housing services' audit trail. A request for information must be made to the database before works are commissioned; this request is recorded on the audit trail system. The system does not close down a request until all the required information is received. This ensures that the system is kept up to date.

Outstanding

There is a question over out-of-hours emergency repairs. This obviously does not fit as neatly into the system as other areas, such as planned maintenance. By the nature of emergency repairs there is a need to respond quickly to problems such as burst pipes etc. In the future it is likely that read-only access to CAD will be provided to the council's contractor partners, so that information can be obtained from the system.

Real benefit

Savings have been made from the implementation of housing services' asbestos policy and management system. Void turnaround time has been dramatically reduced and improved survey efficiency has enabled more effective targeting of resources.

The way forward

The long-term strategy for Islington council is to use housing services' experience to develop and customise management systems specific to individual service area requirements, within a corporate framework. This asbestos management programme will be run by the CAD co-ordinator.

Housing services are now developing an asbestos survey strategy for the communal areas of housing premises such as walkways, stairs, lift shafts, motor, tank and boiler rooms. The survey strategy will be developed in consultation with the CAD co-ordinator.

CASE STUDY 2: A NATIONAL HEALTH SERVICE TRUST: TEES AND NORTH EAST YORKSHIRE

Background

Tees and North East Yorkshire NHS Trust is a community and mental health trust. It does not have any acute illness facilities. The district covers an area from Bridlington to south of Sunderland. They operate out of more than 70 premises, 55 of which are owned by the Trust, 15 are leased and some are rented on a sessional basis for clinics. In some of the leased properties, Trust personnel are responsible for the maintenance of the building. The Trust employs approximately 3250 people, including 35 maintenance personnel. They use up to nine building/ maintenance contract companies and use a preferred list of contractors supplied by the Department for Environment, Food and Rural Affairs (DEFRA).

History of asbestos management

A programme of asbestos surveys and remedial works started in 1984. Much of the survey work was carried out by in-house personnel. Contractors carried out asbestos removal at a number of Trust premises. In 1999, a number of refurbishment and electrical contracts commenced. In at least two premises problems were encountered with debris, contamination and overspray that was not removed at the time of the original asbestos removal contract.

At another leased premises where it was known there was asbestos present, a route for new network cabling was defined which avoided the ACMs. The cablers decided to use an alternative route through sprayed asbestos resulting in contamination of several rooms. The rooms were decontaminated, the sprayed asbestos removed and an alternative fire retardant applied.

A new strategy for managing asbestos

On the basis of the experiences outlined above, the Trust decided to put together a new asbestos policy and to tighten up on control of contractors. A group consisting of the facilities management team and the Trust health and safety officer, with the help of asbestos consultants drew up an action plan. This action plan included, among other items, the following:

- to presume that ACMs are present in all Trust buildings until proven otherwise;

- to update records on the presence of ACMs in Trust premises;

- to clearly mark and maintain ACMs and set priorities for their removal if appropriate; and

- to implement a training programme on asbestos for estates' staff and others.

Funds have been allocated for Type 2 sampling surveys carried out by competent consultants. The survey work is prioritised by reference to the future works programme. The reports from the surveyors are then used to help determine priorities for remedial works.

To tighten control over maintenance and contractors, software for a contractor management system is being developed. This will include site passes, permits-to-work, and site plans.

Plans for recording the asbestos management plan are still in development. Initially, the plans are for a paper system which will, in time, be transferred to a computer-based system.

The asbestos management plan is still in its early stages, but the Trust believe that with a higher standard of survey and a greater awareness of asbestos among its employees, many of the problems encountered previously will be prevented in the future.

CASE STUDY 3:
A LARGE CHEMICAL COMPANY:
BP CHEMICALS

Introduction

BP Grangemouth is a 700 hectare refinery with over 700 buildings, most of which were built between the 1940s and 1980s. There are about 2000 BP employees and more than 600 contractors on site each day. ACMs have been used extensively throughout the site.

The asbestos management system in 1998

In 1998 BP audited their asbestos management system and found that there were opportunities to improve the co-ordination of the programme across the complex. The results showed:

- two different asbestos registers, one for BP Oils and one for BP Chemicals;

- three different analytical companies used on site with different reporting formats;

- limited access to the asbestos registers;

- reactive system: asbestos recorded when disturbed;

- limited surveys, awareness training or labelling of ACMs;

- limited records of the current condition of ACMs; and

- unclear emergency procedures.

A new strategy

Following the audit, BP devised a strategy to achieve an asbestos-safe site. This strategy included the following elements:

- the appointment of a senior manager to be responsible for asbestos management throughout the complex;

- surveys of all plants and buildings to establish if ACMs were present;

- a complex-wide asbestos management plan;

- a computer-based asbestos management system accessible to all personnel on site via the company Intranet; and

- awareness training for all personnel, site and office-based.

CASE STUDY 3

41

Priorities for surveying

As the site was so large, BP first established priorities for surveying. They started with known asbestos areas, those buildings built before 1980, followed by those built between 1985 and 1990 and finally those built after 1990. Initially the strategy was based on carrying out Type 1 surveys, with testing of samples carried out as required by maintenance or other work. However, it became clear that this strategy was not cost-effective and was taking too long to complete. All surveys are now either Type 2 or Type 3 if demolition or major refurbishment is anticipated.

Surveys and analysis of samples are undertaken by one asbestos analytical company, and all asbestos work is undertaken by a single licensed asbestos contractor, who have a permanent presence on site, for other duties as well as asbestos.

A bespoke management system

BP worked with a local IT company to develop a bespoke asbestos management system, which is available to all personnel on site via the company Intranet. The project to devise and implement the management database took three months to complete. The system includes a building register, a sample register, management systems and reports section. Access to the Intranet allows plot plans to be printed with details of asbestos content in each room of a building. Details of the sample results and comments are also available. Actions required to manage the ACMs are logged on the system and summary reports can be pulled off the system for budgeting purposes by each business unit. The system is managed by the asbestos assurance leader and is audited on a regular basis. The register has limited access while the Intranet has unlimited access allowing a large number of interested parties to interrogate the system at anyone time. The system is run by one, part-time, technical clerk.

The asbestos management programme is also audited. There are two external audits per year, which concentrate on 4-5 business units on each visit. Internal audits of the contractors, including the analytical company and the removal contractor, are also conducted. In addition to these, one major internal audit per year is conducted to assess the awareness of site personnel.

Awareness training

Awareness training of personnel is carried out through the use of a 20-minute programme. Given the large number of employees and contractors on site this has been a major task and will continue as new personnel come onto site. Refresher training is planned every two years.

Emergency procedures

Emergency procedures are in place, with the personnel in the incident control room trained to access the asbestos register, so that they can inform the emergency services of the presence of asbestos. On-site emergency services have been trained and there are decontamination facilities available on site at all times.

CASE STUDY 4: FACILITY MANAGEMENT: DRIVERS JONAS FACILITY MANAGEMENT

Introduction

Drivers Jonas is a firm of chartered surveyors whose facility management business has around 500 properties in its portfolio. These properties, although principally in the London and south-east regions, are nationwide.

The premises range from large offices to small individual buildings, many containing ACMs. On any given day a building may require planned or unplanned maintenance work. Although there will be many refurbishment projects, there will be far more unplanned activities, such as the replacement of light fittings, a sudden failure of an air conditioning system, a leaking radiator etc. Any one of these activities could involve the disturbance of an ACM, with exposure to the building trade and resident staff. Drivers Jonas have therefore developed a workable and effective system to control their maintenance contractors across their many premises.

The procedure

- At each premises there is a 'responsible person'. Any fault is reported to the responsible person, who contacts the Drivers Jonas help desk. An 'event' is raised and a request sent electronically or by post to a nominated contractor.

- The contractor has to confirm whether ACMs are present in the work area. This is achieved in a number of ways.

  - Drivers Jonas use two electronic, Internet-based, systems. They have their own simple electronic spreadsheet system, which contractors can access, but have more recently adopted a commercially available Internet-based system to record the asbestos records for the premises under their control. All new premises coming under their control now go on this system. The contractor can check the details of the premises on these systems before arriving on site.

CASE STUDY 4

- In addition the contractor can phone the help desk for confirmation and once on site can access the 'red box'. The 'red box' contains all necessary documentation for the site, including an up-to-date hard copy of the asbestos record. Premises are provided with an updated asbestos record following any remedial works on ACMs.

- As an additional measure, all ACMs are labelled, either with an asbestos warning label, or in areas accessed by the public, a simple red dot.

- The contractors have all received 'tool box' awareness training on asbestos. They are instructed in the procedure, but are informed to be cautious when disturbing materials. If they suspect that it could contain asbestos, but the record does not include this material, they contact the Drivers Jonas help desk.

- If the material to be worked on contains asbestos, they should first see if they can avoid working on it. If they can't, then they should contact the help desk, where arrangements will be made to have the material assessed. It will then be removed, or if this can't be done, any work such as drilling holes that is required will be carried out.

- All work on ACMs is carried out by licensed asbestos removal contractors, irrespective of whether the work falls under the scope of the Asbestos (Licensing) Regulations 1983 as amended.

Survey policy

Their policy is to survey all premises under their control for the presence of ACMs. When new premises come under their control, they request existing survey reports. If there is no survey report, they plan a survey for the site. Until the site has been surveyed, they presume that all materials contain asbestos. For new contracts where there are many premises, they plan their strategy for surveying these, based on occupancy and the timetable for any planned remedial work.

Where survey records do exist, they use these, but undertake independent resurveys of 10% of these as a check on their accuracy.

Mobile performance managers

Mobile performance managers carry out six-monthly checks of the condition of the ACMs. They also check the quality of the maintenance work, the 'red box' for the presence of the asbestos records, and other such matters.

An Internet-based system

Drivers Jonas chose to use an Internet-based system to meet a number of needs:

- to have a high standard of asbestos records, which could be accessed remotely by their contractors;

- to have an easily searchable system;

- to have a system that could give them an audit trail, so that they could check to see whether the contractor had actually accessed the system, the premises and the area where the work is to take place;

- they wanted their contractors to have confidence in the system and to be able to easily use it themselves. They were getting too many 'please check' queries;

- to have a system that could be easily updated.

APPENDIX 1: PLANNING SURVEYS

1   There are several steps to planning and executing your survey strategy. These include:

- looking at health and safety considerations;

- deciding what type(s) of survey to carry out;

- deciding when the surveys should be carried out;

- deciding who will carry out your survey(s);

- deciding, if there are several buildings, which ones get priority;

- information gathering and planning meetings;

- deciding on reporting detail and format.

2   Before carrying out a survey, it is important to carry out an assessment of the risks to the health and safety of surveyors, sampling personnel and other occupants. Risk assessments should be documented and must be available to the site surveyors. Often surveyors will be seeing the site for the first time so will have little chance to assess any site-specific hazards. They may need to rely on information gathered during any preliminary site meeting or walk through the premises. You will need to provide information relating to site emergency procedures and specific hazards, which may include (in addition to asbestos):

- working at heights, in ceiling voids or near fragile roofs;

- working on operable machinery or plant;

- working in confined spaces;

- chemical hazards;

- electrical hazards;

- biological hazards;

- radiation hazards;

- noise hazards; and

- lone working.

Appendix 1

3   The risks to surveyors, sampling personnel and other occupants should be reduced to as low as reasonably practicable. In assessing the risks, the appropriate HSE guidance should be consulted. MDHS100, *Surveying and sampling asbestos-containing material,*[13] contains further general guidance on health and safety risks during surveying and sampling.

What type of survey to carry out

4   The aim of an asbestos survey is, as far as reasonably practicable, to locate and assess the condition of all the ACMs present in the building and its purpose is to present the information collected in a way which allows you to assess and manage the risk. There are three types of survey referred to in MDHS100:[13]

Type 1: Location and assessment survey (presumptive survey)

The purpose of the survey is to locate, as far as reasonably practicable, the presence and extent of any suspect ACMs in the building and assess their condition. This type of survey essentially defers the need to sample and analyse for asbestos until a later time. You will therefore bear potential additional costs of managing some non-ACMs. During this type of survey all areas should be accessed and inspected as far as reasonably practicable or must be presumed to contain asbestos. All materials which are presumed to contain asbestos must be assessed.

Type 2: Standard sampling, identification and assessment survey (sampling survey)

The purpose of this type is to positively identify if a material contains asbestos and the procedures used are the same as for Type 1, except that representative samples are collected and analysed for the presence of asbestos. Samples from each type of suspect ACM found are collected and analysed to confirm or refute the surveyor's judgement. Sampling may take place simultaneously with the survey, or can be carried out as a separate exercise, after the Type 1 survey is complete.

Type 3: Full access sampling and identification survey (pre-demolition/major refurbishment survey)

This type of survey is used to locate and describe, as far as reasonably practicable, all ACMs in the building and may involve destructive inspection, as necessary, to gain access to all areas, including those that may be difficult to reach. A full sampling programme is undertaken to identify possible ACMs and estimates of the volume and surface area of ACMs are made. This type of survey is designed to be used as a basis for tendering for the removal of ACMs from the building before demolition or major refurbishment, so the survey does not assess the condition of the asbestos.

5   The type of survey you choose to carry out will depend on a number of circumstances, but whichever type is used (and it may be a combination), the decision must be clearly recorded, so that there is no confusion at a later date. It is also important that the surveyor is aware of the type of survey he/she is expected to carry out.

Selecting a surveyor

6   The survey(s) can be carried out by in-house personnel or a third party. If the surveys are to be carried out by in-house personnel, you should ensure that they have sufficient training and competence to do so. If you decide to employ a third party, you should ask whether the individual or organisation concerned:

●   have adequate training and experience in such work;

●   can demonstrate independence, impartiality and integrity;

●   have an adequate quality management system; and

●   are carrying out any survey in accordance with recommended guidance, MDHS100 *Surveying, sampling and assessment of asbestos-containing materials,*[13] or similar.

7   To assess whether the third party has the above qualities, you can check whether the organisation is accredited by the United Kingdom Accreditation Service (UKAS) as complying with ISO 17020[15] to undertake surveys for ACMs. When selecting a company, you should ask for information about the number of surveyors qualified to undertake asbestos survey work and ask for a CV for each of the surveyors who may be working on your contract. Some companies may only have one or two suitably qualified and experienced surveyors and you should be assured that any inexperienced surveyors will be closely supervised. The British Institute of Occupational Hygiene (BIOH) qualification gained by passing the P402 examination and assessment of completed survey reports is a basic minimum qualification for individuals carrying out asbestos surveys. The BIOH S301 course followed by examination and oral examination is a more general module covering all aspects of work with asbestos, including surveying. However, gaining the P402 or S301 qualification is only a starting point in achieving competence to carry out surveys. The individual should then spend a period as the assistant surveyor to gain experience from a competent lead surveyor. The period of time shadowing a competent surveyor will vary, but could typically be six months.

8   Alternatively, your organisation can check if an individual surveyor has personal certification for asbestos surveys from a certification body which has been accredited by UKAS under EN45013.[16] A number of organisations, including BIOH, Asbestos Control and Abatement Division (ACAD) and the Royal Institution of Chartered Surveyors (RICS) in association with Asbestos Removal Contractors Association (ARCA), are currently seeking to gain accreditation as certification bodies for an asbestos personal certification scheme. HSE strongly recommends the use of accredited/certified surveyors for complex Type 1, and Type 2 and 3 surveys.

9   If you decide to train someone within the organisation, passing of the BIOH P402 or S301 modules with some practical experience, should be a satisfactory starting point for anyone carrying out surveys.

10   You will need to identify a laboratory to analyse any bulk samples taken as part of a Type 2 or Type 3 survey. Information on laboratories undertaking this work can be obtained through UKAS, or BIOH via their consultancy directory. Asbestos Testing and Consulting (ATAC), part of ARCA, also have details of member laboratories carrying out this type of work. The laboratory should be able to demonstrate its competence to carry out bulk asbestos analysis (eg staff training records, certificates from external training providers, participation in quality assurance schemes, satisfactory performance in national proficiency testing programmes, accreditation to ISO 17025[17] or an equivalent). The Asbestos in Materials Scheme (AIMS) is the UK national proficiency testing programme for bulk asbestos analysis. UKAS can provide up-to-date information on those laboratories which are accredited to ISO 17025[17] for bulk analysis, and the Committee for Fibre Measurement (CFM) can provide details of those laboratories having a satisfactory performance in AIMS. **It will be mandatory by 2004 for those organisations using an external company to undertake analysis of samples to identify asbestos to use a laboratory accredited to ISO 17025.[17] Those who use their own employees will also need to meet the same criteria under this standard.**

11   An important issue during the selection of an external surveyor/consultancy is the extent of their professional indemnity insurance cover. Errors during asbestos surveys can lead to costly remedial works and expensive court cases, both civil and criminal. It is therefore important to establish that the surveyor's cover is commensurate with the risk. Professional indemnity cover for carrying out this type of work should be in the region of £5 million, but will depend on the extent of the liability, and could therefore be lower or higher. Where there is additional risk due to the potential losses associated with a decrease in the value of a property following the discovery of asbestos after purchase, the professional indemnity cover will need to be much higher; that is high enough to cover the potential loss. For example, a commercial property owner intends to purchase a property in central London and commissions a survey. The owner should be sure that the surveyor has enough cover to compensate the losses associated with a decrease in the value of the property, if asbestos is discovered following a survey which stated it was free from asbestos, or asbestos is located in areas which were missed during the survey.

Information gathering

12   There are a number of steps that can be taken before the survey to ensure that the survey is carried out in a safe, efficient manner. The better the preparation, the less likely it will be that the surveyor will have to make several return visits to gather further information or gain access to a locked office/store/boiler room. The steps are:

●   to inform employees;

●   to hold planning meetings;

●   to give the surveyor building plans and specifications;

- to hold a pre-survey meeting with surveyor;

- to have a preliminary walk-through.

Informing employees

13   The first step is to communicate with employees. Managers will need to be aware that a surveyor will be on site and may need access to restricted areas, so that someone can be on hand to unlock doors or, if necessary, provide an escort for the surveyor. If the workforce is unionised then the union health and safety representative should be consulted (under the Safety Representatives and Safety Committee Regulations 1977[18]), and may be given the opportunity to take part in any pre-survey planning meetings. If the employees do not belong to a union then the employees' representative should fulfil that role (under the Health and Safety (Consultation with Employees) Regulations 1996[19]). Employees and their representatives are likely to have information which may be pertinent to the survey, particularly where there are employees with long service records, who may well remember ACMs being installed or previous asbestos removal works. Maintenance personnel and occupational health and safety professionals will also have useful information.

Planning meetings

14   It may be wise to hold one or several planning meetings; some may be internal for information-gathering; at least one should be with the surveyor on site to discuss site hazards and risk assessments, as well as to exchange information regarding the survey itself.

Building plans and specifications

15   Both original and up-to-date plans, where available, will be very useful for the surveyor. They will provide the basis upon which the surveyor can plan his/her work, and may also be used in the final report to indicate the presence of asbestos. The date of the original construction and those of any subsequent refurbishments or additions will give an important indication of whether asbestos is likely to be present.

16   It is also useful if building materials specifications are available to the surveyor. This will provide a good indication to the surveyor of the materials used, although this is not definitive as builders may have altered specifications during the construction process, or used cheaper materials than those specified.

17   Information about any refurbishments or additional building works carried out since the original construction, such as plans and specifications will also be useful in helping to determine the likely presence of ACMs.

18   Copies of previous asbestos surveys and details of previous asbestos removal projects should be provided if they exist. These should not be used to exclude areas for survey, but should be regarded as an additional information source. Many removal jobs in the past were not carried out to a high specification and quantities of asbestos debris may remain in an area supposedly now free of asbestos.

Pre-survey meeting with surveyor

19   During a site pre-survey meeting with the surveyor, the surveyor should be introduced to key people in the organisation who will be able to help during the survey in providing keys for access, escorts if required, and any additional information which may be needed during the survey. The surveyor should also be given information about site hazards, both structural and process, and any pertinent site risk assessments. They should be made aware of any site safe systems of work that may be relevant to the work they will be carrying out. They will need, for example, to be aware of any electrical hazards which may have a bearing on whether they can bring a camera on site, or the need for protective clothing, if enclosed areas such as ducts and roof voids need to be checked. They also need to be informed of site procedures for fire, first aid etc.

Preliminary walk-through

20   A brief walk-through with the surveyor is useful to allow the surveyor to become familiar with the layout of the premises and to gain an appreciation of the size of the project. They may also be able to give a rough guide to the number of samples that may need to be taken for analysis, on the basis of the walk-through.

Reporting format and medium

21   Before the survey is carried out a decision will be required on the survey report format and detail to be included. You will need to decide whether the report should just detail where ACMs are, or report on each area (ie information on the walls, ceiling and floor of each area, and a list of all accessible areas or just those not accessed etc). You will also need to decide whether photographs of all ACMs should be taken or just a representative number (ie if there is a panel in the same position in every room, do you want a photograph of each one?). The options for the report format are:

● hard copy;

● computer-based electronic copy;

● your Intranet; and/or

● an Internet site managed by a third party.

22   A small company with few ACMs or presumed ACMs on its premises and maintenance activities carried out by in-house personnel may not need to establish an electronic asbestos record, as a paper-based system will be easy to manage. Medium-sized organisations with a number of ACMs on the premises and a mixture of contractors and in-house maintenance staff likely to work on the premises will need to consider the use of a computer-based system, for ease of updating and providing information to those carrying out work on the premises. Where large organisations have an Intranet system available to employees, this may well be the best way of disseminating information throughout the organisation. If well-managed, it will ensure that the information is up to date and immediately accessible to those who need it. Another alternative is to post your organisation's survey on a registered Internet site. These are sites managed by a third party, and are subject to a subscription. The information held on these sites is then available to third parties, for example, contractors, who can then download the information before working on your premises.

23   If a decision has been made to use a computer-based asbestos record and management system, then it will make sense to receive the survey report electronically so that it can more easily be transferred into the system. It may be possible for the surveyor to use the same software and provide the report, following approval, directly into the management software. A hard copy which can later be incorporated into a system will be more useful if you have yet to decide on the format your management system is going to take. Whatever format is decided on, consider long-term storage of the information, the need to update it when situations change and its accessibility.

24   Another consideration when deciding on report format is the use of drawings. If they are used, can they be incorporated into an electronic report? The identification of areas on the drawings also needs to be determined. If each area is already numbered or otherwise identified then these forms of identification should be used in the survey report. However, if an area is known by the activity carried out there, or the people who work there, this will present difficulties in the future if activities change or move around. In these cases an identification system should be created which can be put on drawings and in the report, so that there is no confusion over the areas being reported on.

APPENDIX 2: SURVEY REPORT, MATERIAL ASSESSMENT AND ALGORITHM

1　　This appendix describes what your survey report should contain and the use of material assessment algorithms. The surveyor should provide this assessment for you with the survey report. The use of a material assessment algorithm allows each ACM or presumed ACM to be scored and ranked in order of their ability to release fibres. If these ACMs or presumed ACMs are not disturbed then nobody can be exposed. You therefore also need to consider the likelihood of your employees or others disturbing the ACMs. To do this you need to carry out a priority assessment algorithm, which is described in Appendix 3.

Survey report

2　　MDHS100, *Surveying, sampling and assessment of asbestos-containing materials*,[13] the guidance prepared for those carrying out surveys, includes a list of what should be contained in a survey report. This list is reproduced here to give you information about what to expect from a survey report.

3　　The final report, depending on the type of survey undertaken, may contain the following sections:

- general site and survey information;

- the survey report;

- a sample analysis report;

- a material assessment/report.

4　　General site and survey information should include:

- the name and address of the organisation carrying out the survey;

- the names of the surveyors;

- the name and address of the person who commissioned the survey;

- the name and address of the premises surveyed;

- the date of the report;

- the date of the survey;

Appendix 2

- the purpose, aims and objectives of the survey;

- a description of the areas included in the survey;

- a description of any areas excluded from the survey;

- the survey method used (MDHS100[13] and/or other documented procedures);

- the type of survey undertaken (Type 1, Type 2 or Type 3) and, if more than one type is used, where they apply within the premises;

- any variations or deviations from the method; and

- agreed exclusions and inaccessible areas.

5   The survey report should include a set of marked-up plans (quality will depend on what was available) and a table, spreadsheet or database containing the following descriptors for the ACMs or presumed ACMs:

- location (eg building identifier, floor number or level, room identifier and position);

- extent (area, length, thickness and volume, as appropriate);

- product type (coating, board etc);

- level of identification (presumed, strongly presumed or identified);

- accessibility/vulnerability;

- amount of damage or deterioration; and

- surface treatment (if any).

6   It should also include the material assessment score or category (high, medium, low or very low) given.

7   For Type 2 and Type 3 surveys, a sample analysis report should also be attached and include:

- the name and address of the laboratory carrying out the bulk identification;

- a reference to the method used;

- the laboratory's current United Kingdom Accreditation Service (UKAS) accreditation for bulk asbestos analysis/sampling and accreditation number;

- a table or appendix summarising the results of the bulk analysis, including asbestos found or not found and types identified, by sample identifier;

- dates the bulk analysis was carried out and reported by the laboratory; and

- the names and signatures of the analyst and any countersigning person.

Material assessment and algorithm

The risk assessment includes a material assessment and a priority assessment.

The material assessment looks at the type and condition of the ACM and the ease with which it will release fibres if disturbed.

The priority assessment (Appendix 3) looks at the likelihood of someone disturbing the ACM.

8   The material assessment is an assessment of the condition of the ACM, or the presumed ACM, and the likelihood of it releasing fibres in the event of it being disturbed in some way. This material assessment will give a good initial guide to the priority for management as it will identify the materials which will most readily release airborne fibres if disturbed. However, there are other factors to take into account when prioritising action. These are considered in the priority assessment which is described in Appendix 3.

9   MDHS100[13] recommends the use of an algorithm to carry out the material assessment, and contains an example. The algorithm is a numerical way of taking into account several influencing factors, giving each factor considered a score. These scores can then be totalled to give a material assessment score. The use of algorithms is not infallible, but the assessment process is clear for all to see, so if discrepancies arise, it should be possible to track back through the assessment process to find the root of the error. The algorithm shown in MDHS100[13] considers four parameters that determine the risk from an ACM: that is the ability to release fibres if disturbed. These four parameters are:

• product type;

• extent of damage;

• surface treatment; and

• asbestos type.

10   Each of the parameters is scored and added to give a total score between 2 and 12:

• materials with scores of 10 or more should be regarded as high risk with a significant potential to release fibres if disturbed;

• those with a score between 7 and 9 are regarded as medium risk;

• materials with a score between 5 and 6 are low risk; and

• scores of 4 or less are very low risk.

11   The material assessment algorithm shown in MDHS100[13] is reproduced here. You should now read on to the priority assessment in Appendix 3.

Table 2 Material assessment algorithm

Sample variable	Score	Examples of scores
Product type (or debris from product)	1	Asbestos reinforced composites (plastics, resins, mastics, roofing felts, vinyl floor tiles, semi-rigid paints or decorative finishes, asbestos cement etc)
	2	Asbestos insulating board, mill boards, other low density insulation boards, asbestos textiles, gaskets, ropes and woven textiles, asbestos paper and felt
	3	Thermal insulation (eg pipe and boiler lagging), sprayed asbestos, loose asbestos, asbestos mattresses and packing
Extent of damage/ deterioration	0	Good condition: no visible damage
	1	Low damage: a few scratches or surface marks; broken edges on boards, tiles etc
	2	Medium damage: significant breakage of materials or several small areas where material has been damaged revealing loose asbestos fibres
	3	High damage or delamination of materials, sprays and thermal insulation. Visible asbestos debris
Surface treatment	0	Composite materials containing asbestos: reinforced plastics, resins, vinyl tiles
	1	Enclosed sprays and lagging, asbestos insulating board (with exposed face painted or encapsulated), asbestos cement sheets etc
	2	Unsealed asbestos insulating board, or encapsulated lagging and sprays
	3	Unsealed laggings and sprays
Asbestos type	1	Chrysotile
	2	Amphibole asbestos excluding crocidolite
	3	Crocidolite
Total score		

APPENDIX 3 - PRIORITY ASSESSMENT AND ALGORITHM

1   The material assessment (see Appendix 2) identifies the high risk materials, that is, those which will most readily release airborne fibres if disturbed. It does not automatically follow that those materials assigned the highest score in the material assessment will be the materials that should be given priority for remedial action. Management priority must be determined by carrying out a risk assessment which will also take into account factors such as:

- maintenance activity;

- occupant activity;

- likelihood of disturbance;

- human exposure potential.

The risk assessment includes a material assessment and a priority assessment.

The material assessment (Appendix 2) looks at the type and condition of the ACM and the ease with which it will release fibres if disturbed.

The priority assessment looks at the likelihood of someone disturbing the ACM.

2   The risk assessment can only be carried out with detailed knowledge of all the above. Although a surveyor may have some of the information which will contribute to the risk assessment and may be part of an assessment team, you, as the dutyholder under CAW,[5] are required to make the risk assessment, using the information given in the survey report and your detailed knowledge of the activities carried out within your premises. The risk assessment will form the basis of the management plan, so it is important that it is accurate.

Maintenance activity

3   The first and most important factor which must be taken into consideration is the level of maintenance activity likely to be taking place in an area. Maintenance trades such as plumbers and

Appendix 3

electricians are the group who the duty to manage is primarily trying to protect. There are two types of maintenance activity, planned and unplanned. Planned work can be assessed and carried out using procedures and controls to reduce exposure to asbestos. Unplanned work requires the situation to be dealt with as found and the controls that can be applied may be more limited. The frequency of maintenance activities also need to be taken into account in deciding what management action is appropriate.

Occupant activity

4   The activities carried out in an area will have an impact on the risk assessment. When carrying out a risk assessment the main type of use of an area and the activities taking place within it should be taken into account. For example a little used storeroom, or an attic, will rarely be accessed and so any asbestos is unlikely to be disturbed. At the other end of the scale, in a warehouse lined with asbestos insulating board panels, with frequent vehicular movements, the potential for disturbance of ACMs is reasonably high and this would be a significant factor in the risk assessment. As well as the normal everyday activities taking place in an area, any secondary activities will need to be taken into account.

Likelihood of disturbance

5   The two factors that will determine the likelihood of disturbance are the extent or amount of the ACM and its accessibility/vulnerability. For example, asbestos soffits outdoors are generally inaccessible without the use of ladders or scaffolding, are unlikely to be disturbed. The asbestos cement roof of a hospital ward is also unlikely to be disturbed, but its extent would need to be taken into account in any risk assessment. However if the same ward had asbestos panels on the walls they would be much more likely to be disturbed by trolley/bed movements.

Human exposure potential

6   The human exposure potential depends on three factors: the number of occupants of an area, the frequency of use of the area, and the average time each area is in use. For example, a school boiler room is likely to be unoccupied, but may be visited daily for a few minutes. The potential for exposure is much less than say in a classroom lined with asbestos insulating board panelling, which is occupied daily for six hours by 30 pupils and a teacher.

Priority assessment algorithms

7   Taking all these factors into account in a logical, consistent manner is difficult. Using an algorithm will help you to produce priority assessments that have taken the factors into account in a consistent way. An example of an algorithm for use in making the priority assessment is shown in Table 2. The number of factors relevant at any one site needs to be carefully considered, as the more factors included in an algorithm, the lower the influence of the most important risk factors becomes, and this may produce anomalies. For this reason it is recommended that the number of factors that are

scored is limited to four, the same as the number of factors in the material assessment (Appendix 2). There is no single set of factors that can be recommended that will apply equally to all types of premises. *Therefore four general headings have been used and one or more factors can be taken into account and averaged under each heading to suit the circumstances.* If you choose to use more than one factor under a general heading, then average the scores under that heading, rounding up where necessary.

8   The scores from the material assessment (ie the condition of the ACM or presumed ACM) are added to the scores of the priority assessment (the likelihood of disturbance), to give the overall risk assessment. Risk assessment scores for different ACMs can then be compared to develop your action plan. In many circumstances the scores will be similar, making decisions more difficult. For example a boiler house with asbestos pipework insulation in poor condition may get the same or similar risk assessment score to an office with asbestos insulating board in reasonably good condition. This is simply because the ACM in the boiler house received a higher score than the ACM in the office because the ACM in the boiler house was in poor condition. However, the priority assessment for the office will get a higher score than the boiler house since the office is occupied more often. Add the scores together for the material and priority assessments, and you get similar scores. If this is the case then you may decide that the office needs doing first because it is used daily. On the other hand you may decide that the poor condition of the ACM in the boiler house means that it should be done first.

9   If the office was a classroom, the young age of the occupants may be a deciding factor. Appendix 4 contains worked examples that may help you. Algorithms are provided to help you, but they are best guesses and will often require you to make your own additional judgements.

Table 3 Priority assessment algorithm (read page 60, paragraph 7 on score averaging before using this algorithm)

Assessment factor	Score	Examples of score variables
Normal occupant activity		
Main type of activity in area	0	Rare disturbance activity (eg little used store room)
	1	Low disturbance activities (eg office type activity)
	2	Periodic disturbance (eg industrial or vehicular activity which may contact ACMs)
	3	High levels of disturbance, (eg fire door with asbestos insulating board sheet in constant use)
Secondary activities for area	As above	As above
Likelihood of disturbance		
Location	0	Outdoors
	1	Large rooms or well-ventilated areas
	2	Rooms up to 100 m^2
	3	Confined spaces
Accessibility	0	Usually inaccessible or unlikely to be disturbed
	1	Occasionally likely to be disturbed
	2	Easily disturbed
	3	Routinely disturbed
Extent/amount	0	Small amounts or items (eg strings, gaskets)
	1	$\leq$10 m^2 or $\leq$10 m pipe run.
	2	>10 m^2 to $\leq$50 m^2 or >10 m to $\leq$50 m pipe run
	3	>50 m^2 or >50 m pipe run
Human exposure potential		
Number of occupants	0	None
	1	1 to 3
	2	4 to 10
	3	>10
Frequency of use of area	0	Infrequent
	1	Monthly
	2	Weekly
	3	Daily
Average time area is in use	0	<1 hour
	1	>1 to <3 hours
	2	>3 to <6 hours
	3	>6 hours
Maintenance activity		
Type of maintenance activity	0	Minor disturbance (eg possibility of contact when gaining access)
	1	Low disturbance (eg changing light bulbs in asbestos insulating board ceiling)
	2	Medium disturbance (eg lifting one or two asbestos insulating board ceiling tiles to access a valve)
	3	High levels of disturbance (eg removing a number of asbestos insulating board ceiling tiles to replace a valve or for recabling)
Frequency of maintenance activity	0	ACM unlikely to be disturbed for maintenance
	1	$\leq$1 per year
	2	>1 per year
	3	>1 per month

APPENDIX 4:
WORKED EXAMPLES OF PRIORITY RISK ASSESSMENTS

In these examples it is assumed that you have been provided with the material assessment score by the surveyor and you are now carrying out the priority assessments. For each algorithm the material and priority assessment scores are added together.

Example 1: Primary school

An independent primary school has been surveyed and three ACMs have been identified:

- lagging on the boiler and associated pipework in the boiler room;

- asbestos insulating board panelling on the inside walls of a temporary classroom; and

- an asbestos cement roof on a temporary classroom building erected in the 1970s.

The survey report included a material assessment for each of the materials, including a material assessment score. The school bursar and the caretaker were charged with carrying out priority risk assessments to help in the development of a management plan.

They looked in detail at the locations of each of the ACMs identified and compiled their risk assessments using the risk assessment algorithm in Table 3. Their completed algorithms for each of the ACMs are shown below.

Appendix 4

Table 4 Priority assessment algorithm for lagging on the boiler and associated pipework in the boiler room

Priority assessment algorithm			
Assessment factor	*Variable(s) selected*	*Score for each variable*	*Overall score*
NORMAL OCCUPANT ACTIVITY			
Main type of activity in area	Low disturbance activities (checking safety controls on boiler once per day)	1	1
LIKELIHOOD OF DISTURBANCE			
Location	Rooms up to 100 m^2 - boiler room 6 m x 7 m	2	
Accessibility	Occasionally likely to be disturbed - don't need to disturb ACM to carry out checks but may inadvertently disturb	1	
Extent/amount	small boiler and single 10 m pipe run	2	average = 2
HUMAN EXPOSURE POTENTIAL			
Number of occupants	None	0	
Frequency of use of area	Daily - daily safety control checks	3	
Average time area is in use	<1 hour - few minutes once a day	0	average = 1
MAINTENANCE ACTIVITY			
Type of maintenance activity	Minor disturbance - potential for disturbance during annual servicing of boiler	0	
Frequency of maintenance activity	>1 per year - annual service + 1 breakdown visit per year	2	average = 1
Total priority assessment score			5
Material assessment score (supplied by surveyor)			11
Total of material and priority assessment scores			16

Table 5 Priority assessment algorithm for asbestos insulating board panelling on the inside walls of a temporary classroom

Priority assessment algorithm			
Assessment factor	*Variable(s) selected*	*Score for each variable*	*Overall score*
NORMAL OCCUPANT ACTIVITY			
Main type of activity in area	High levels of disturbance, children running in and out of classroom, knocking wall panels, wall displays	3	3
LIKELIHOOD OF DISTURBANCE:			
Location	Rooms up to 100 m^2 - classroom 10 m x 9 m	2	
Accessibility	Routinely disturbed - easily accessible to young children	3	
Extent/amount	57 m^2 area of wall paneling	3	average = 3
HUMAN EXPOSURE POTENTIAL			
Number of occupants	>10-30 children, 1 teacher and 1 classroom assistant	3	
Frequency of use of area	Daily	3	
Average time area is in use	>6 hours	3	average = 3
MAINTENANCE ACTIVITY			
Type of maintenance activity	Low disturbance - occasional redecoration	1	
Frequency of maintenance activity	≤1 per year	1	average = 1
Total priority assessment score			10
Material assessment score (supplied by surveyor)			7
Total of material and priority assessment scores			17

Table 6 Priority assessment algorithm for asbestos cement roof on a temporary classroom building erected in the 1970s

Priority assessment algorithm			
Assessment factor	**Variable(s) selected**	**Score for each variable**	**Overall score**
NORMAL OCCUPANT ACTIVITY			
Main type of activity in area	Rare disturbance activity (eg little used store room)	0	0
LIKELIHOOD OF DISTURBANCE			
Location	Outdoors	0	
Accessibility	Usually inaccessible or unlikely to be disturbed	0	
Extent/amount	>50 m^2	3	average = 1
HUMAN EXPOSURE POTENTIAL			
Number of occupants	None	0	
Frequency of use of area	Infrequent	0	
Average time area is in use	<1 hour	0	average = 0
MAINTENANCE ACTIVITY			
Type of maintenance activity	Minor disturbance (eg possibility of contact when gaining access)	0	
Frequency of maintenance activity	ACM unlikely to be disturbed for maintenance	0	average = 0
Total priority assessment score			1
Material assessment score (supplied by surveyor)			4
Total of material and priority assessment scores			5

Primary school - discussion of scores

In terms of priority the asbestos cement is not of great concern, whereas the scores for the boiler room and the asbestos insulating board wall panels in the classroom are similarly high. The classroom has been scored slightly higher partly because of the greater number of people potentially at risk, but also because of the greater likelihood of the asbestos insulating board being disturbed.

The scoring system makes the assessment process transparent so people can see how priorities were decided. People may not always agree with the result, but the scoring system allows a debate about the decisions and why they were made. Other factors may also need to be taken into account.

The boiler house lagging and asbestos insulating board panelling had similar total scores. However the boiler house lagging had a higher material assessment score, whereas the classroom panelling had a higher priority assessment score. This suggests that the boiler room is of higher risk because the material can more easily be disturbed. However, the classroom had a higher priority assessment score because of the 30 young children compared to one boiler house operative. Therefore the classroom is of greater priority and would require immediate action due to the high risk of the asbestos insulating board being disturbed. This example shows the need to carefully consider the results of the algorithms and fully understand the risk factors that provide the total scores.

Example 2: Chemical plant

A survey has identified fours ACMs in one chemical plant on a larger complex. The plant manager has been asked to conduct priority risk assessments and develop a management plan.

The four ACMs identified were:

- lagging on pipework on an overhead pipe bridge over an internal road;

- asbestos insulating board ceiling tiles in the control room;

- spray on the underside of the roof of a redundant warehouse; and

- lagging on a reaction vessel.

The risk assessment algorithms are shown below.

Table 7 Priority assessment algorithm for lagging on pipework on an overhead pipe bridge over an internal road

Priority assessment algorithm			
Assessment factor	*Variable(s) selected*	*Score for each variable*	*Overall score*
NORMAL OCCUPANT ACTIVITY			
Main type of activity in area	Rare disturbance activity	0	0
LIKELIHOOD OF DISTURBANCE			
Location	Outdoors	0	
Accessibility	Occasionally likely to be disturbed	1	
Extent/amount	>10 m to ≤50 m pipe run	2	average = 1
HUMAN EXPOSURE POTENTIAL			
Number of occupants	None	0	
Frequency of use of area	Daily	3	
Average time area is in use	>6 hours	3	average = 2
MAINTENANCE ACTIVITY			
Type of maintenance activity	Minor disturbance	0	
Frequency of maintenance activity	≤1 per year	1	average = 1
Total priority assessment score			4
Material assessment score (supplied by surveyor)			10
Total of material and priority assessment scores			14

Table 8 Priority assessment algorithm for asbestos insulating board ceiling tiles in the control room

Priority assessment algorithm			
Assessment factor	Variable(s) selected	Score for each variable	Overall score
NORMAL OCCUPANT ACTIVITY			
Main type of activity in area	Low disturbance activities	1	1
LIKELIHOOD OF DISTURBANCE			
Location	Room up to 100 m^2	2	
Accessibility	Occasionally likely to be disturbed	1	
Extent/amount	>50 m^2	3	average = 2
HUMAN EXPOSURE POTENTIAL			
Number of occupants	1-3	1	
Frequency of use of area	Daily	3	
Average time area is in use	>6 hours	3	average = 2
MAINTENANCE ACTIVITY			
Type of maintenance activity	Low disturbance	1	
Frequency of maintenance activity	>1 per year	2	average = 2
Total priority assessment score			7
Material assessment score (supplied by surveyor)			6
Total of material and priority assessment scores			13

Table 9 Priority assessment algorithm for spray on the underside of the roof of a redundant warehouse

Priority assessment algorithm

Assessment factor	Variable(s) selected	Score for each variable	Overall score
NORMAL OCCUPANT ACTIVITY			
Main type of activity in area	Rare disturbance	0	0
LIKELIHOOD OF DISTURBANCE			
Location	Large room or well-ventilated area	1	
Accessibility	Usually inaccessible or unlikely to be disturbed	0	
Extent/amount	>50 m^2	3	average = 1
HUMAN EXPOSURE POTENTIAL			
Number of occupants	None	0	
Frequency of use of area	Infrequent	0	
Average time area is in use	<1 hour	0	average = 0
MAINTENANCE ACTIVITY			
Type of maintenance activity	Minor disturbance	0	
Frequency of maintenance activity	ACM unlikely to be disturbed for maintenance	0	average = 0
Total priority assessment score			1
Material assessment score (supplied by surveyor)			12
Total of material and priority assessment scores			13

71

Table 10 Priority assessment algorithm for lagging on a reaction vessel

Priority assessment algorithm			
Assessment factor	*Variable(s) selected*	*Score for each variable*	*Overall score*
NORMAL OCCUPANT ACTIVITY			
Main type of activity in area	Periodic disturbance	2	2
LIKELIHOOD OF DISTURBANCE			
Location	Large room or well-ventilated area	1	
Accessibility	Occasionally likely to be disturbed	1	
Extent/amount	>50 m^2	3	average = 2
HUMAN EXPOSURE POTENTIAL			
Number of occupants	1-3	1	
Frequency of use of area	Daily	3	
Average time area is in use	>6 hours	3	average = 2
MAINTENANCE ACTIVITY			
Type of maintenance activity	Medium disturbance	2	
Frequency of maintenance activity	>1 per year	2	average = 2
Total priority assessment score			8
Material assessment score (supplied by surveyor)			9
Total of material and priority assessment scores			17

Chemical plant - discussion of scores

From the results of the priority risk assessment, it can be seen that the lagging on the reaction vessel should be given the highest priority for management action. The lagging is disturbed relatively frequently and would release fibres relatively easily.

The assessment scores for the other three ACMs are very similar so would require some interpretation to decide on priorities. The warehouse is the least likely to require attention, as it is no longer in use. As long as it is locked and nobody disturbs the ACM in there, there is no risk. This would obviously change if it were decided to recommission the building.

The asbestos insulating board tiles in the control room had a low material assessment score and a low priority assessment score as the tiles are in good condition and are rarely disturbed apart from perhaps changing light bulbs or cleaning light fittings, so immediate attention is not required.

The overhead pipe bridge had a high material assessment score, indicating that the lagging is in bad condition. The overall risk assessment score was reduced as it is rarely disturbed and is outdoors. The roadway is in constant use and as the lagging is likely to deteriorate, action would need to be taken in the medium term.

Example 3: Hospital

A hospital ward block has had four ACMs identified during a survey. They were:

- lagging on pipes in underfloor ducts;

- asbestos insulating board panels on fire doors in the corridors;

- vinyl floor tiles throughout the block; and

- asbestos insulating board ceiling tiles throughout the block.

The estates department in conjunction with a member of management are conducting risk assessments to establish priorities for their management plan. The risk assessment algorithms are shown below.

Table 11 Priority assessment algorithm for lagging on pipes in underfloor ducts

Priority assessment algorithm			
Assessment factor	Variable(s) selected	Score for each variable	Overall score
NORMAL OCCUPANT ACTIVITY			
Main type of activity in area	Rare disturbance activity	0	0
LIKELIHOOD OF DISTURBANCE			
Location	Room up to 100 m^2	2	
Accessibility	Usually inaccessible or unlikely to be disturbed	0	
Extent/amount	>50 m pipe run	3	average = 2
HUMAN EXPOSURE POTENTIAL			
Number of occupants	None	0	
Frequency of use of area	Infrequent	0	
Average time area is in use	<1 hour	0	average = 0
MAINTENANCE ACTIVITY			
Type of maintenance activity	Medium disturbance	2	
Frequency of maintenance activity	>1 per year	2	average = 2
Total priority assessment score			4
Material assessment score (supplied by surveyor)			10
Total of material and priority assessment scores			14

Table 12 Priority assessment algorithm for asbestos insulating board panels on fire doors in the corridors

Priority assessment algorithm			
Assessment factor	*Variable(s) selected*	*Score for each variable*	*Overall score*
NORMAL OCCUPANT ACTIVITY			
Main type of activity in area	High levels of disturbance	3	3
LIKELIHOOD OF DISTURBANCE			
Location	Room up to 100 m^2	2	
Accessibility	Routinely disturbed	3	
Extent/amount	<10 m^2	1	average = 2
HUMAN EXPOSURE POTENTIAL			
Number of occupants	>10	3	
Frequency of use of area	Daily	3	
Average time area is in use	>6 hours	3	average = 3
MAINTENANCE ACTIVITY			
Type of maintenance activity	Minor disturbance	0	
Frequency of maintenance activity	≤1 per year	1	average = 1
Total priority assessment score			9
Material assessment score (supplied by surveyor)			7
Total of material and priority assessment scores			16

Table 13 Priority assessment algorithm for vinyl floor tiles throughout the block

Priority assessment algorithm			
Assessment factor	Variable(s) selected	Score for each variable	Overall score
NORMAL OCCUPANT ACTIVITY			
Main type of activity in area	Low disturbance	1	1
LIKELIHOOD OF DISTURBANCE			
Location	Large rooms or well-ventilated areas	1	
Accessibility	Unlikely to be disturbed	0	
Extent/amount	>50 m^2	3	average = 1
HUMAN EXPOSURE POTENTIAL			
Number of occupants	>10	3	
Frequency of use of area	Daily	3	
Average time area is in use	>6 hours	3	average = 3
MAINTENANCE ACTIVITY			
Type of maintenance activity	Minor disturbance	0	
Frequency of maintenance activity	Annual polishing of floor tiles	1	average = 1
Total priority assessment score			6
Material assessment score (supplied by surveyor)			1
Total of material and priority assessment scores			7

Table 14 Priority assessment algorithm for asbestos insulating board ceiling tiles throughout the block

Priority assessment algorithm			
Assessment factor	*Variable(s) selected*	*Score for each variable*	*Overall score*
NORMAL OCCUPANT ACTIVITY			
Main type of activity in area	Low disturbance activities	1	1
LIKELIHOOD OF DISTURBANCE			
Location	Large rooms or well-ventilated areas	1	
Accessibility	Usually inaccessible or unlikely to be disturbed	0	
Extent/amount	>50 m^2	3	average = 1
HUMAN EXPOSURE POTENTIAL			
Number of occupants	>10	3	
Frequency of use of area	Daily	3	
Average time area is in use	>6 hours	3	average = 3
MAINTENANCE ACTIVITY			
Type of maintenance activity	Low disturbance	1	
Frequency of maintenance activity	≤1 per year	1	average = 1
Total priority assessment score			6
Material assessment score (supplied by surveyor)			6
Total of material and priority assessment scores			12

Hospital - discussion of scores

From the overall scores reached for each ACM it can be seen that the vinyl floor tiles are extremely low risk and will not require any action unless they are to be removed. The asbestos insulating board ceiling tiles are in good condition and rarely disturbed, so again immediate management action is not required.

The asbestos insulating board panels on the fire doors are routinely disturbed and are damaged as a consequence of trolleys hitting the panels, therefore they have a relatively higher score. The corridors are in constant use so they would be a priority needing action in the short term.

The underfloor ducts also have a high overall score, but the risk here is when the ducts are opened and the lagging disturbed during maintenance activities, rather than on a day to day basis. Management action is also a priority here and would need to be scheduled taking into account the maintenance activities.

Management options and guidance on their selection is discussed in Appendix 5.

APPENDIX 5:
MANAGEMENT OPTIONS AND
SELECTION OF MANAGEMENT
OPTIONS

Management options

1   Appendix 2 and 3 showed you how to carry out a risk assessment. This appendix discusses management of the ACMs you have now prioritised, some requiring immediate action. This is not your full management plan, but options for dealing with your ACMs. It presents measures which will be needed in all cases where ACMs are present, and further options for managing the condition of your ACMs. Flow charts to help you decide which option is most suitable are presented at the end of this appendix.

Measures needed in all cases where ACMs are present

- communicate with employees, contractors and others;

- monitor the condition of the ACM;

- put a safe system of work in place (discussed in paragraph 82).

Options for managing the condition of your ACMs

- label the ACM;

- colour code the ACM.

- protect/enclose the ACM;

- seal/encapsulate the ACM;

- repair the ACM;

- remove the ACM.

Measures needed in all cases where ACMs are present

Communicate with employees

2   It is important to communicate with employees throughout the asbestos management process, from inspection of the premises through to the decision-making about management of your ACMs. Employees and others should be made aware of the location of any ACMs in the buildings they work in if they are liable to disturb them. This is particularly important for maintenance workers who

Appendix 5

may directly disturb ACMs while working. Means of communicating with contractors who come on site to carry out work must also be set up to prevent them disturbing ACMs without taking proper precautions.

3   Take care when communicating with your employees and others about the presence of ACMs. It is important that you give the positive messages about management of ACMs emphasising that the steps you are taking will reduce the risk of exposure and ill health. Remember the key messages at the front of this guidance. These will help you reassure your employees and others. Encourage them to be aware of the presence of ACMs and to report any damage.

Monitor the condition of ACMs

4   ACMs which are in good condition, sealed and/or repaired, and are unlikely to be disturbed, may be left in place. Often this is a safer option than removal, which will result in the ACMs being disturbed. If they are left in place, the condition of the ACMs will have to be monitored regularly and the results recorded. A useful way of monitoring the condition of your ACMs is to take photographs, which can be used to compare the condition over time. When the condition of the ACM starts to deteriorate, remedial action can be taken. The time period between monitoring will vary depending on the type of ACM, its location and the activities in the area concerned, but would not be expected to be more than 12 months in most cases. ACMs in remote locations, with little or no routine activity, can be inspected infrequently. For example, an asbestos insulating board ceiling in a remote unoccupied building may only need inspecting once every 12 months or even less frequently if the building is rarely entered. ACMs in locations where there is a lot of activity will need more frequent monitoring. For example, asbestos insulating board panels on the walls of a constantly used corridor may need inspecting once a month. Monitoring would involve a visual inspection, looking for signs of disturbance, scratches, broken edges, cracked or peeling paint and debris. Where deterioration has occurred, a recommendation on what remedial action to take would need to be made. This may be a case of resealing the surface of the ACM, but if there is evidence that the ACM is being disturbed on a frequent basis; say for example a forklift truck was hitting an asbestos cement panel on a wall, the decision may be made to remove the panel or at least protect it by putting up a suitable barrier after clearing any visible debris. The reason for the constant disturbance also needs investigating. As well as protecting the ACM you would also want to consider how you can stop the forklift truck from hitting the panel and its barrier, if one is put up. You should also encourage employees to report any new damage to ACMs that they become aware of.

Options for managing the condition of your ACMs

Labelling and colour-coding of ACMs

5   Where an ACM is going to be left in place, one option would be to label the material, or in the case of pipework colour-code the insulation. This may work in a factory environment, but may not be acceptable in a suite of offices or in public areas, for example, retail premises. The decision to label or not will in part depend on

confidence in the administration of the asbestos management system and whether communication with workers and contractors coming to work on site is effective. You should decide on a standard for labelling to ensure consistency of use on the ACMs. If the asbestos record is up to date and control over maintenance workers and contractors is tight, through, for example, the use of permit-to-work systems, then labelling may be seen as unnecessary. Labelling and colour coding alone should not be relied on as control measures in themselves. They may become dirty, obscured or fall off and therefore should only be used as a back-up measure. It is important that good lines of communication between the managers of the asbestos management system and workers and contractors should be maintained, so that they have access to good, accurate information about ACMs in the premises.

Protection/enclosure of ACMs

6   Protecting ACMs means the construction or placing of a physical barrier of some sort to prevent accidental disturbance of the ACM. This may mean placing a bollard in front of a wall panel of asbestos insulating board to prevent accidental damage by fork lift truck movements. Enclosing the ACM involves the erection of a barrier around it, which should be as airtight as possible to prevent the migration of asbestos fibres from the original material. This will involve sealing the edges and corners of the barrier. Enclosing the ACM is a good option if it is in reasonable condition, but it may still be vulnerable to damage. Potential problems for the future should be borne in mind when choosing this option. If, for example, the ACM may be subject to water damage or if access is likely to be required to the enclosure for maintenance or repairs, the removal option may be more sensible and less costly in the longer term.

7   If enclosure is chosen as the desired management option it is important that the existence of the ACM behind the enclosure is noted in the asbestos record and that the condition of the enclosure is monitored and the results of the inspection recorded. Labelling to indicate the presence of the hidden ACM is another option.

8   Another consideration when enclosing asbestos is if the ACM was in place to provide fire resistance, then the material from which the enclosure is made or its design should not compromise that resistance. Seek advice from the local fire authority.

9   If the ACMs to be enclosed fall within the scope of the Asbestos (Licensing) Regulations 1983 (as amended)(see paragraphs 19 to 23) and the enclosure building is liable to disturb the ACM, this work should be done by a licensed asbestos removal contractor.

Seal or encapsulate the ACM

10   There are two types of encapsulants: bridging encapsulants which form a durable layer adhering to the surface of the ACM; and penetrating encapsulants which are designed to penetrate into the ACM before hardening and locking the material together to give the ACM additional strength. Bridging encapsulants include high build elastomers, cementitious coatings and polyvinyl acetate (PVA). The different types of

encapsulants available will suit different circumstances and ACMs. High build elastomers can provide substantial impact resistance as well as elasticity, especially when they incorporate a reinforcing membrane. These types of encapsulants are reported to provide up to 20 years of life if undisturbed. Cementitious coatings are generally spray-applied and are compatible with most asbestos applications. They provide a hard-set finish, but may crack over time. PVA is used for sealing of asbestos insulating board and may be spray or brush applied. It is not suitable for use on friable ACMs such as insulation or sprayed coatings. PVA will only provide a very thin coating and may not be suitable as a long-term encapsulant. Penetrative encapsulants are spray-applied and will penetrate friable asbestos materials, strengthening them as well as providing an outer seal. The fire-resistant properties of the encapsulant will be an important consideration if the function of the ACM was to provide fire resistance. Encapsulation of an ACM is only suitable if the ACM is in sound condition and can take the additional weight of the encapsulant without delamination; that is the coming away of the ACM from the substrate it was covering.

11   The preparation and application of encapsulants requires a certain amount of skill and must, in virtually all cases, be carried out by asbestos removal contractors licensed by HSE under the Asbestos (Licensing) Regulations[20] (see paragraphs 19 to 23).

Repair the ACM

12   To be readily repairable, the damage must be slight, therefore repair should be restricted to patching/sealing small areas and making good slight damage to enclosures which are protecting ACMs. If the ACM is to be repaired, there are a number of methods that can be employed depending upon the type of material. Small areas of damaged pipe or boiler lagging can be filled with non-asbestos plaster and if necessary wrapped with calico (cotton cloth). Small areas of damaged sprayed asbestos can be treated with encapsulant and, if necessary, an open mesh scrim of glass fibre or calico reinforcement used. Damaged asbestos panelling or tiles can be sprayed with PVA sealant or a similar type of sealant such as an elastomeric paint. PVA will only provide a very thin coating and may not be suitable as a long-term encapsulant, particularly where there is significant damage. A higher performance elastomeric coating may be needed. ACMs that are unsealed, while not damaged, may be treated with a sealant to prevent deterioration of the exposed surface. Asbestos cement should be sealed using an alkali-resistant and water-permeable sealant. If impermeable paint is used on one side of a product without back painting, it can cause premature failure of the ACM. It is important to consider the fire protection afforded by any ACMs that are treated to ensure that the treatment does not adversely affect the fire-retardant properties. Unless the work is on ACMs not covered by the Licensing Regulations, or the work is very minor, repair work should be undertaken by a licensed asbestos removal contractor (see paragraphs 19 to 23).

Remove the ACM

13   Where ACMs have been identified and are not in good condition, or are in a vulnerable position and liable to damage, the options discussed in paragraphs 6-12 should be explored first. Where it is not practical to repair, enclose or encapsulate the ACMs, they will need to be removed. ACMs will also need to be removed if the area is due to undergo refurbishment which will disturb the ACM, or where a building is going to be demolished. This work will generally have to be undertaken by licensed asbestos removal contractors, unless of course the ACM is asbestos cement or other highly bonded materials not covered by the scope of the Licensing Regulations (see paragraphs 19 to 23).

Selection of management options

14   As mentioned in paragraph 1 some of the management options will need to be taken with all ACMs; others will provide an either/or choice. The following flow charts which follow, together with explanatory notes, outline procedures for the selection of appropriate remedial measures. These charts are taken from previous government advice.[21]

15   Figure 11 summarises the decisions to be made when asbestos materials are first identified, and leads to a decision to manage the materials in place or directs attention to Figures 12-14 which give further directions for deciding how to deal with different types of ACM. To use each chart, start at the top of the page and move downwards. Diamond-shaped boxes represent questions which must be answered yes or no; rectangles represent the recommended remedial action.

Figure 11: Materials suspected of containing asbestos

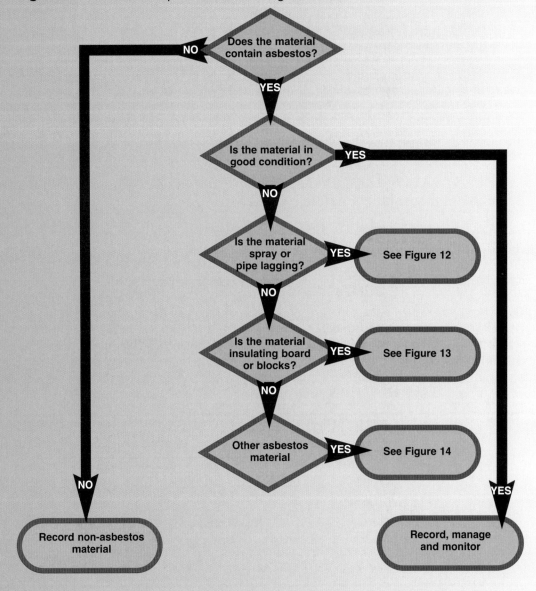

Figure 12: Sprayed asbestos coatings and pipe and vessel insulation

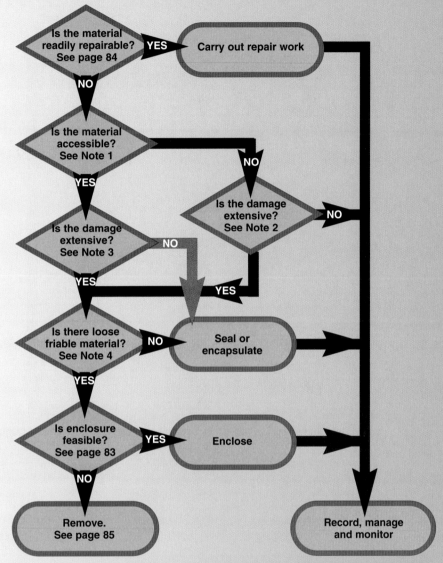

1 Is the material accessible and vulnerable to further accidental or deliberate damage from adjacent repair or maintenance, impact by people, vehicles, objects or vandalism?

2 If the damage is slight and the ACM is not easily accessible, remedial work is unlikely to be necessary. The damage should be monitored and your decision reviewed if circumstances change (eg the area becomes accessible).

3 If the damage is superficial, eg slight cracking to pipework insulation or deteriorated surface finish, then answer 'no' to this question. If, for example, the insulation is starting to come away from the pipework or the spray coating appears to be loose in places, then answer 'yes' to this question. If there is debris on the floor or other surfaces then this will need removing following appropriate precautions.

4 The damage may be extensive, but if the material is generally sound without friable material or loose pieces, then sealing/encapsulation may be possible.

Figure 13: Asbestos insulating board and insulating blocks

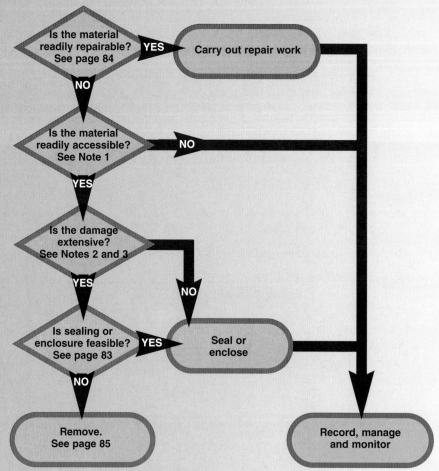

1 Is the material accessible and vulnerable to further accidental or deliberate damage from adjacent repair or maintenance, impact by people, vehicles, objects or vandalism? If the damage is not easily accessible, remedial work may not be necessary. The damage should be monitored and your decision reviewed if circumstances change (eg the area becomes accessible).

2 If the damage is superficial, eg slight cracking to pipework insulation or deteriorated surface finish, then answer 'no' to this question. If, for example, the insulation is starting to come away from the pipework or the spray coating appears to be loose in places, then answer 'yes' to this question.

3 If there is debris on the floor or other surfaces then this will need removing following appropriate precautions.

Figure 14: Other asbestos materials (Read Notes 1 and 2 first)

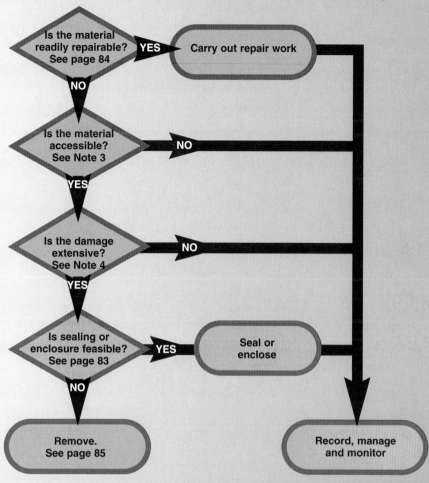

1 This chart covers products not included in Figures 12 and 13, such as asbestos cement, textiles, gaskets, ropes and encapsulated products such as vinyl and thermoplastic tiles, roofing felts etc. **Materials which are encapsulated in a resilient matrix will have limited ability to release fibres, therefore asbestos in reinforced plastics, vinyls, resins, rubber, mastics, bitumen, paints, flexible plasters and cements have little opportunity to release fibres unless the matrix is removed (eg degraded, dissolved or burnt) or subject to high levels of abrasion (eg use of power tools).** Management of these types of materials so maintenance workers do not use abrasive methods and power tools is usually sufficient to minimise airborne asbestos releases. Sealing may be considered if there is evidence of routine wear and abrasion. The flow chart shows you the decisions to be considered if remedial action is deemed to be necessary. However, unless the damage is significant or they are in a vulnerable position, urgent remedial action is unlikely to be necessary and you should simply remove these products, following the correct precautions (paragraph 19-23), when they come to the end of their useful life, or before refurbishment or demolition.

2 **Products which are less well encapsulated (eg asbestos textiles and gaskets),** will release fibres more readily and use of controlled work methods by maintenance workers and enclosure or sealing to prevent damage may be necessary in some circumstances.

continued overleaf

3 Is the material accessible and vulnerable to further accidental or deliberate damage from adjacent repair or maintenance, impact by people, vehicles, objects or vandalism?

4 If the damage is slight, remedial work is unlikely to be necessary. The damage should be monitored and your decision reviewed if circumstances change (eg the area becomes accessible).

APPENDIX 6: MANAGING ASBESTOS CONTRACTORS, AND ANALYTICAL LABORATORIES

Selecting licensed contractors

1   The importance of careful selection of a suitable contractor to undertake repair or removal of ACMs cannot be overestimated. This type of work is licensed by HSE and only those firms holding a current licence should undertake this type of contract (see paragraphs 19-23 for exceptions). If the work does not require the contractor to hold a licence you should still ensure that they are competent to do the work and follow CAW.[5] Below is a series of steps you can take to help ensure you select the right company to carry out the work you require. Work with asbestos is not cheap. If you obtain a quotation much lower than any other you have received, you should make sure they have fully understood the nature and scope of the work. They could simply be good value or may have misunderstood the extent of the work. On the other hand, they could be cutting corners, which may mean the whole job could end up costing a lot more than you had anticipated, with the possibility of the spread of asbestos leading to contamination and poor workmanship necessitating calling in different contractors to finish a poor job. **Notification to the enforcing authority is required 14 days in advance of the start of any licensable work on ACMs.**

2   A list of all contractors holding a licence is available from HSE's Asbestos Licensing Unit in Edinburgh for a small administration charge. It is organised by region, so finding local contractors should be relatively easy. About half of all licensed asbestos removal firms are members of trade associations. There are two trade associations for asbestos removal contractors, ARCA (Asbestos Removal Contractors Association) and ACAD (Asbestos Control and Abatement Division of TICA, Thermal Insulation Contractors Association). These two trade associations can also provide lists of their members.

3   Other sources of information may include your local authority (who may have a list of contractors that they have vetted and appear on their preferred bidder list), local surveyors, architects and occupational hygienists. There may be other companies locally who have had work carried out and may be able to provide information about their contractors.

Appendix 6

91

4   From these initial sources of information, select about five companies. Contact these companies and ask for the following details:

- a copy of their licence;

- details of their public and employer liability insurances;

- training records for their employees;

- references from recently completed contracts;

- details of any action taken against them by HSE/LA (prosecutions, improvement notices or prohibition notices).

5   Details of action taken against companies and individuals is also available on HSE's website at www.hse.gov.uk/prosecutions. Most prosecutions for asbestos-related work will be found under 'construction industry', sub-sector 'insulation work activities'. The database only includes cases taken since 1999. Details of prohibition notices and improvement notices issued by HSE are also available at www.hse.gov.uk/notices, although this only includes notices from July 2001.

6   In order to ensure that the contractors are all quoting on the same basis, it would be helpful to prepare an information pack. This pack should contain information about:

- the scope of the work to be carried out;

- the results of the relevant parts of the survey of the premises;

- site plans;

- information about site-based hazards that the contractors may need to take into account;

- site safety rules including permit-to-work regimes;

- access to the working area including siting of decontamination facilities and waste skips;

- access to water and power supplies;

- use of site facilities;

- time constraints;

- penalty clauses;

- whether the work area is unoccupied or if there will be people working near it;

- emergency procedures;

- arrangements for liaison during the contract;

- whether the work will be supervised/managed by a third party; and

- any other issues that might affect the way the contractors will carry out their work.

7   The information pack should also include a list of the information you require to be included in the quote to be prepared. The list below indicates the range of information you may want from the contractor in addition to the price for the work:

- the estimated duration of the contract;

- the estimated number of personnel expected to be on site;

- risk assessment(s) for the job including estimated exposures for removal operatives;

- plan of work (method statement). This should include information about:

   - the repair/removal methods to be used;

   - the type of equipment to be used;

   - the type of personal protective equipment to be used;

   - a plan of the enclosure, including siting of the negative pressure units, the entry/exit arrangements, siting of the decontamination unit and waste skip, and transiting routes (if the decontamination unit is not directly connected to the enclosure);

   - monitoring arrangements, including air sampling inside and outside the enclosure;

- emergency procedures; and

- a possible start date.

8   To prepare a detailed quote, the contractor will almost always need to visit the site to assess the job. You should make sure that the contractors are aware of any constraints on their work which may affect costs, such as working times, and any site safety training requirements. If at a later stage you find that you have omitted some-thing you think may affect pricing, you should contact all the contractors and ask that they bear it in mind when preparing their quote. If you give them new information after they have quoted, ask them to submit a requote if they feel that it will materially affect the way they work. This is important as the quotes must be prepared on the basis of valid information.

9   Once all the quotes have been received these should be reviewed. Look for the common features, such as the number of workers and the duration of the contract, and the plan of work indicating the methods to be used. If there is one which has a much shorter estimated duration, fewer workers and a lower price than most, it is possible that this contractor has misjudged the extent of the work. For example, you may find at a later date that asbestos debris has been left, which may lead to other tradespeople or your own employees being exposed to asbestos. A big clean-up operation involving more asbestos contractors may ensue, with bad publicity for your company and a loss of confidence on the part of employees. At the very least you are likely to be faced with a bill for 'extras' which may outweigh the initial saving anticipated by using the cheapest contractor.

Requirements for asbestos removal workers

Each asbestos removal worker has to undergo an initial training period which includes attendance on a course as well as practical on-the-job training. In addition each worker must attend annual refresher training. Each time they attend training they receive a training certificate, which must be available for inspection. Supervisors should have been experienced asbestos removal workers before training to become a supervisor. They also have to attend annual supervisor refresher training. All asbestos removal workers have to attend medicals every two years. Operators also have to have a face-fit test for the type of respirator they use. There is no set time period in which these tests have to be repeated, but the Approved Code of Practice for licensed work[11] states that they will need to be repeated if their face shape changes, or if there is a change in the model of respirator being used.

Asbestos removal work, what to expect

Preliminary meeting

10   Once the tenders have been reviewed and a contractor selected, it is advisable to set up a preliminary meeting some time before the start date of the project. This will allow the exchange of any further information between the two parties and detailed arrangements to be made, before the contractor notifies the work to the enforcing authority. You should also look at the supporting information such as training records, medical certificates and face-fit tests for respirators. If these are not available it may be because the contractor does not retain a regular workforce, so may use unskilled, inexperienced workers to carry out the work, which is likely to lead to poor quality work and the possibility of problems during the contract.

11   At this stage you should also ask to see other paperwork including copies of examination and test certificates for plant to be used during the contract, for example:

- the decontamination unit;

- negative pressure units;

- type H vacuum cleaners;

- electrical generators; and

- wetting equipment.

12   Notification is required 14 days before the start date in order to allow the enforcing authority to review the method statement and to visit the site if necessary. There may also be a requirement to submit a notification under the Construction (Design and Management) Regulations 1994.[9] At this stage, you should clarify with the contractor the communication arrangements during the project, and which laboratory will be employed to carry out the inspections necessary to issue a certificate of reoccupation. A certificate of reoccupation, is required to show that the work area (including the transit route and surrounding area) is free from asbestos and that the air is free from detectable levels of asbestos.

Table 15: Typical exposures during work with asbestos lagging, coating and asbestos insulating board (AIB)

Technique	Typical exposure f/ml	Comments
Controlled wet stripping of lagging and sprayed coatings	Up to 1	Thorough soaking of lagging with a wetting agent followed by careful removal
Uncontrolled dry stripping of lagging	1-100	Stripping dry or where dry patches are encountered
Uncontrolled dry stripping of sprayed coatings	Up to 1000	Stripping dry or where dry patches are encountered
Careful removal of whole AIB boards	Up to 3	Unscrewing (with shadow vacuuming) with the spray application of a wetting agent on unsealed surfaces
Breaking and ripping out AIB	5-20	Carried out with no unscrewing
Drilling AIB overhead	5-10	No local exhaust ventilation (LEV)
Drilling vertical columns	2-5	No LEV
Use of a jigsaw on AIB	5-20	No LEV
Hand sawing AIB	5-10	No LEV

Asbestos removal methods

13   In almost all cases, asbestos should be removed using controlled wetting techniques. For lagging or sprayed asbestos, this should consist of multipoint injection of wetting liquids; for asbestos insulating board a wetting agent can be applied using a spray. However, removal of asbestos insulating board can be carried out using local exhaust ventilation during nail/screw removal and spraying before handling. When using injection techniques, time must be allowed for the wetting agent to be dispersed throughout the ACM and this should be taken into account by the contractor when calculating the duration of the contract. Wherever possible, tight time constraints placed on contractors should be avoided, as this is one example of where corners may be cut to save time. This leads to inadequate (or no) wetting of the ACM. If the material is not wetted, the airborne fibre levels in the enclosure increase beyond the capacity of the respirators to control exposure below the control limits. This massively increases the risk to health of the asbestos removal workers and also increases the risk of exposure to others outside the enclosure if the integrity of the enclosure is compromised in any way.

14   If on examination, the method of work seems to suggest that a dry stripping method is to be employed, question the contractor closely about why controlled wetting techniques have not been indicated, and what alternative methods of control will be used. If there are conditions within your site that are influencing the contractor's decision to use wet stripping methods, you should carefully consider what you can do to assist the contractor so controlled wet stripping methods can be used. For example if the contractor is citing an electrical hazard within the area to be enclosed, you should do all you can to ensure that the electrical hazard is isolated for the duration of the stripping contract. There is almost no situation where a short-term alternative power supply cannot be used.

Enclosures

15   You should also check the plan of work for details of how the contractor will ensure asbestos is not inadvertently spread. Any spread of asbestos may contaminate other parts of your property and expose either your employees or other people you have responsibility for. The normal way this is done is to erect an enclosure and ensure it is kept under adequate negative pressure.

Viewing panels

16   It is also advisable to monitor the work of the contractor. You should check the plan of work includes providing viewing panels to allow the contractors' own management to supervise the work and yourselves to monitor compliance with their plan of work.

Monitoring the contractor

17   To obtain information on the actual performance of your contractor to feed back into your selection procedure and to ensure the contractor is not putting people under your responsibility at risk, there are some simple checks you can carry out. These are as follows:

- be present at the smoke test and witness that the enclosure does not leak. At this time you can also check the plant and equipment specified in the plan of work is present and within its current test date;

- during the work make use of the viewing panels to check operatives are wearing the correct personal protective equipment and using the controlled wetting technique specified in the plan of work;

- try to be present when the analytical laboratory declares the enclosure clean. You can check the enclosure looks clean and the ACMs have been removed yourself (through the viewing panels where possible);

- check the area again after the enclosure has been removed, making sure that the area is visually clean and that the ACMs have been removed.

Selecting analytical laboratories

18   When the work with asbestos has been carried out, and the area thoroughly cleaned and visually inspected by the contractor, an analyst has to be engaged to carry out a visual inspection and air sampling to ensure that the work area is ready for reoccupation. If the analyst is satisfied that the area is safe for reoccupation he/she will provide a certificate of reoccupation (the Approved Code of Practice looks at this in more detail). It is strongly recommended that you, as the client, rather than the contractor, engages the services of an analyst. This prevents the possibility of a conflict of interests arising, as could be the case if the analyst is employed by the contractor. There is a duty on the employer under CAW that any laboratory engaged to carry out any air sampling for determination of asbestos fibres in air, should be accredited to ISO 17025.[17] A list of laboratories accredited to ISO 17025 is available from UKAS or from their website. All accredited laboratories must be members of the Regular Interlaboratory Counting Exchanges scheme (RICE). The Institute of Occupational Medicine publishes the RICE list and this gives details of laboratories' accreditations.

19   Laboratories that participate in RICE and AIMS (Appendix 1, paragraph 10) can be found on the Health and Safety Laboratory website. Information is also available from ATAC (Asbestos Testing and Consultancy, part of ARCA) or from BIOH (British Institute of Occupational Hygienists). It would be prudent to discuss the contract with laboratories early on in the proceedings to ensure that you can find one that is able to do the work, and is likely to be available at the time the project is due for completion.

Managing asbestos repair/removal contracts

20   Managing an asbestos repair or removal contract can be a time-consuming and complex business, depending on the size of the contract. For all but the most straight-forward of jobs, it may be worthwhile considering employing a laboratory to at least help in the management of the contract. Laboratories will offer a range of services from providing a visual inspection and air sampling, drawing up specifications for tender packages and reviewing quotations, supervising the smoke test of an enclosure, carrying out reassurance monitoring outside an enclosure during the asbestos repair/removal, through to complete management of the project from start to finish.

21   As with asbestos removal contractors it is important that when selecting a laboratory to provide a service, you take care to employ one who has the expertise to carry out the work you require. For those offering a full supervisory management of an asbestos project, a licence issued by HSE's Asbestos Licensing Unit is required. Further information on those laboratories holding a supervisory licence is available from the HSE's Asbestos Licensing Unit in Edinburgh.

REFERENCES

1   *A short guide to managing asbestos in premises* Leaflet INDG223(rev3) HSE Books 2002 (single copy free or priced packs of 10ISBN 0 7176 2564 8)

2   *Introduction to asbestos essentials: Comprehensive guidance on working with asbestos in the building maintenance and allied trades* HSG213 HSE Books 2001 ISBN 0 7176 1901 X

3   *Asbestos essentials task manual: Task guidance sheets for the building maintenance and allied trades* HSG210 HSE Books 2001 ISBN 0 7176 1887 0

4   *Controlled asbestos stripping techniques for work requiring a licence* HSG189/1 HSE Books 1999 ISBN 0 7176 1666 5

5   *Control of Asbestos at Work Regulations 2002* The Stationery Office 2002

6   *Health and Safety at Work etc Act 1974* The Stationery Office 1974

7   *Management of health and safety at work. Management of Health and Safety at Work Regulations 1999. Approved Code of Practice and guidance* L21 (Second edition) HSE Books 2000 ISBN 0 7176 2488 9

8   *Workplace (Health, Safety and Welfare) Regulations 1992* SI 1992/3004 The Stationery Office 1992 ISBN 0 11 025804 5

9   *Construction (Design and Management) Regulations 1994* SI 1994/3140 The Stationery Office 1994 ISBN 0 11 043845 0

10   *The management of asbestos in non-domestic premises. The Control of Asbestos at Work Regulations 2002. Approved Code of Practice and guidance* L127 HSE Books 2002 ISBN 0 7176 2382 3

11   *Work with asbestos insulation, asbestos coating and asbestos insulating board. Control of Asbestos at Work Regulations 2002. Approved Code of Practice* L28 (Fourth edition) HSE Books 2002 ISBN 0 7176 2563 X

12   *Work with asbestos which does not normally require a licence Approved Code of Practice* L27 (Fourth edition) HSE Books 2002 ISBN 0 7176 2562 1

13   Surveying, sampling and assessment of asbestos-containing materials MDHS100 HSE Books 2001 ISBN 0 7176 2076 X

14   Julian Peto et al 'Continuing increase in mesothelioma mortality in Britain' The Lancet 1995 345 March 4 535-539

15   ISO 17020: 1998 General criteria for the operation of various types of bodies performing inspection

16   BS 7513:1989, EN 45013:1989 General criteria for certification bodies operating certification of personnel

17   BS EN ISO/IEC 17025:2000 General requirements for the competence of testing and calibration laboratories

18   Safety Representatives and Safety Committees Regulations 1977 SI 1977/500 The Stationery Office

19   Health and Safety (Consultation with Employees) Regulations 1996 SI 1996/1513 The Stationery Office 1996 ISBN 0 11 054839 6

20   Asbestos (Licensing) Regulations 1983 SI 1983/1649 The Stationery Office 1983 ISBN 0 11 037649 8 as amended by Asbestos (Licensing)(Amendment) Regulations 1998 SI 1998/3233 The Stationery Office 1998 ISBN 0 11 080279 9

21   Asbestos and man-made mineral fibres in buildings, Practical Guidance DETR 1999 ISBN 0 7277 2835 0

22   BS 5415-2.2:Supplement No. 1:1986 Safety of electrical motor-operated industrial and commercial cleaning appliances. Particular requirements. Specification for vacuum cleaners, wet and/or dry. Specification for type H industrial vacuum cleaners for dusts hazardous to health

23   Working with asbestos cement HSG189/2 HSE Books 1999 ISBN 0 7176 1667 3

FURTHER INFORMATION

HSE InfoLine
Tel: 08701 545500
Fax: 02920 859260
e-mail: hseinformationservices@natbrit.com
or write to:
HSE Information Services
Caerphilly Business Park
Caerphilly CF83 3GG
www.hse.gov.uk

Asbestos Control and Abatement Division (ACAD)
TICA House
Allington Way
Yarm Road Business Park
Darlington
Co Durham DL1 4QB
Tel: 01325 466704
www.tica-acad.co.uk

Asbestos Removal Contractors Association (ARCA)
ARCA House
237 Branston Road
Burton upon Trent
Staffordshire DE14 3BT
Tel: 01283 531126
www.arca.org.uk

Asbestos Testing and Consultancy (ATAC)
ARCA House
237 Branston Road
Burton upon Trent
Staffordshire DE14 3BT
Tel: 01283 531126
www.arca.org.uk/atac

British Institute of Occupational Hygienists (BIOH)
Suite 2, Georgian House
Great Northern Road
Derby DE1 1LT
Tel: 01332 298087
www.bioh.org

Further information

United Kingdom Accreditation Service
21-47 High Street
Feltham
Middlesex TW13 4UN
Tel: 020 8917 8400
www.ukas.com

Health and Safety Laboratory
Broad Lane
Sheffield S3 7HQ
Tel: 0114 2892920
www.hsl.gov.uk

Printed and published by the Health and Safety Executive C120 2/04